BLACKBURN CENTRAL LIBRARY

C000026462

BLACKBURN DISTRICT L.T.

AC

1. JAN 96

03. JAN 9.

01. MAR 93   13. JUN 94

30. MAR 92 L.   21. MAY 93   04. JUL 94

08. APR 92   10. NOV 93   28. JUL 94
                                02. 09. 94
30.   29. DEC 93
                                06. OCT 94
                19 Jan 94 R
06. JUL   28. FEB 94   26. OCT 94

                22. MAR 94   16. MAR 95
14. OCT   06. APR 95
12. NOV 92
                21. APR 94   09. MAY 95
10. DEC 92   29. NOV 95

AUTHOR	CLASS
FLOOD, M.	333·794

TITLE

Energy without end

Lancashire
County
Council

THE LANCASHIRE LIBRARY.
Library Headquarters,
143, Corporation St.,
PRESTON PRI 2TB.

a30118 050889918b

Energy Without End

Author: **Michael Flood**
Editor: **Michael Harper**
Design: **David Caines**

Acknowledgements

I should like to thank the following who have commented on early drafts of this report or provided research support and technical assistance: Mark Barrett, Stewart Boyle, the BWEA, David Cope, Jonathan Doig, David Hall, Jim Halliday, Vicki Hird, Ilex Associates, Athena Lamnisos, Tim Kirby, Nigel Mortimer, David Olivier, Tadj Oreszczyn, Eileen Owen, Walt Patterson and Jonathon Scurlock.

My special thanks to Mike Harper, Liz Peltz, Simon Roberts and Yvonne Spyrou for editing the text and to David Caines for coordinating layout and publication.

Thanks to Friends of the Earth Trust Limited for the research which has been drawn on for this report.

333·7

12/91
PcT

050889918

Photographs

Front cover: *Sun* Gabe Palmer/ACE; *Leaves* Paul Craven/ACE; *Waves* Auschromes/ACE. **Back cover:** *Solar water-heating, Tel Aviv* Michael Flood; *City at night* Keith Kent/Science Photo Library **Page 3:** Gabe Palmer/ACE; Michael Flood; Paul Craven/ACE; David Hall **Page 4:** Dan Farber/Science Photo Library; Michael Flood; Keith Kent/ Science Photo Library; Highlands and Islands Enterprise **Page 5:** After Image/ACE; ETSU; Peter Menzell/Science Photo Library; ETSU **Page 6:** Martin Bond/Science Photo Library; Wind Energy Group; **Pages 10 & 11:** Hank Morgan/Science Photo Library **Page 17:** ETSU **Page 24:** Michael Flood **Page 25:** Martin Edwards; Michael Flood; ETSU **Page 29:** Michael Flood; Michael Flood **Page 31:** Michael Flood; Michael Flood; ETSU **Page 35:** ETSU; The Creative Company/MKDC **Page 36:** ETSU; Michael Flood **Page 38:** Martin Bond/Science Photo Library; ETSU **Page 40:** ETSU **Page 43:** Kvaerner Brug **Page 44:** Les Duckers/Wave Energy Group **Page 48:** Friends of the Earth **Page 53:** Michael Flood; Vantage **Pages 54 & 55:** Michael Flood **Page 56:** David Olivier **Page 59:** Michael Flood **Page 63:** Michael Flood **Page 64:** L.Campbell/NHPA

July 1991
© Friends of the Earth
Published by Friends of the Earth Ltd
ISBN 0 905966 87 2

Friends of the Earth
26-28 Underwood Street
London N1 7JQ

Biographical Note

Dr Michael Flood *BSc PhD*
is a freelance lecturer, writer and researcher with special interest in the study of new and renewable energy technologies and in the problems of implementing technology policy. He has acted as a consultant to Friends of the Earth (1976-82) and has given evidence to a number of official commissions and parliamentary committees. He held a two year Lectureship in Technology at the Open University (1983-85), and has since been a Tutor-Counsellor on the Technology Foundation Course. He has produced a number of books, including *Solar Prospects* (1983), *Energy Without End* (1986) and *The End of the Nuclear Dream* (1988). He writes regularly on waste and recycling issues for the *Warmer Bulletin*.

He has served on the Committee of the UK Solar Energy Society (1985-90), and is a member of the British Wind Energy Association. He has made a number of study trips abroad: visiting Thailand, India, Nepal, Cote d'Ivoire, Burkina Faso, Ghana and Egypt and the United States on a US Government International Visitors' Programme. He has recently been awarded a Winston Churchill Travel Fellowship to study the environmental movement in Eastern Europe. Additionally, he is in the process of setting up a non-profit-making information service, *Powerful Information*, for groups in developing countries.

Designed and typeset by Friends of the Earth's in-house production team. Printed by LAC Litho. Printed on paper which contains 45% woodfree unprinted, 45% woodfree printed waste and 10% virgin fibre (de-inked). Made by St.Regis (Silverton Mill) and supplied by Paperback Limited.

energy without end

contents

contents

Author's Note

In late 1985, Friends of the Earth asked me to investigate the potential for renewable energy in the UK. The result was a book entitled *Energy Without End*, which was published the following year. In the book I argued that Britain could meet a fifth or more of its energy needs from indigenous renewable energy resources by 2025, given the political will - and provided also that it implemented a vigorous programme of cost-effective energy efficiency measures designed to cut primary energy use by a third. Wind energy, biofuel waste, and geothermal heat provided the bulk of the renewable energy, with smaller contributions from solar and water power (hydro-electricity, tidal and wave energy).

Five years on, there has been little progress towards the goal of adopting a more sustainable, less environmentally damaging energy path, despite the clear indications that all is not well with current policies based primarily on fossil fuels. Public attitudes have changed: there is now widespread concern over the environmental implications of the unregulated burning of coal, oil and gas, and the fissioning of uranium, and real alarm at the prospect of major climate upheaval brought about by the release of carbon dioxide and other greenhouse gases. The need for change is more urgent than ever.

This book, then, is a sequel to the first *Energy Without End*. It reassesses the prospects for renewable energy in line with the latest estimates of resource size and technical performance, and proposes a somewhat more radical approach in the light of what we now know about global warming. It argues that Britain could cut its dependence on fossil fuels by half through a combination of cost-effective energy efficiency improvements and low impact renewable energy technologies. The discussion is focussed more on policy issues rather than technology, because it is here that the real problems exist. Many of the technical problems are well on the way to being sorted out.

No one can have any illusions as to just how difficult it is going to be for the UK to change direction and adopt a renewable energy path. But then the consequences of not modifying our behaviour and reducing our demands are even more daunting. This generation more than any before has the power to turn the planet into an uninhabitable wasteland. But it also has the means to feed, clothe and house all of the world's peoples, without destroying the miraculous web of life that makes our planet so unique. In this respect, it is for the countries of Europe, North America and Japan to set a model for others to follow, for it is these countries that have devoured so much of the world's resources and precipitated the environmental crisis that we now confront. With the loss of habitat and species diversity the countries of the developing world are not blameless, but they have been more the victims of their circumstance and unwilling participants in the wholesale destruction that has taken place.

As the environmental problems become more pressing, the need to take positive action grows even more urgent. This book is about what one country, the UK, can do to play its part in this mission.

Michael Flood
May 1991

1. Introduction

"Sunlight, in its many guises, is the force that has shaped and driven the miraculous living fabric of this planet for billions of years. It embodies the best engineering, the widest safety margins, and the greatest design experience we know. It provides amply for our needs, yet limits our greed. It is safe, eternal, universal, and free. It falls justly and equitably on South and North, East and West. It increases autonomy, fosters diversity and does not hurt the balance of payments."

Ted Taylor, leading US nuclear physicist and former bomb designer

1.1 Renewable Energy

Inexhaustible Energy

The amount of solar energy absorbed by the Earth and its atmosphere in just one year is equivalent to one hundred times the energy stored in the world's proven reserves of fossil fuels. If we could capture just one ten thousandth of this energy, using solar collectors, specially designed buildings, wind and water turbines, wave energy converters, trees and other fuel crops, we could supply more useful energy in a year than we currently get from burning coal, oil and gas. Unlike fossil fuels, renewable energy cannot be exhausted.

Renewable sources of energy have been harnessed throughout history. Today, they play a vital role in the world (see Figure 1.1), particularly in developing countries. Over the last two decades a whole range of more efficient, advanced renewable energy technologies has been developed. Yet, industrialised countries, having grown dependent on fossil fuels, are only just beginning to take advantage of the abundant opportunities to shift to renewable energy.

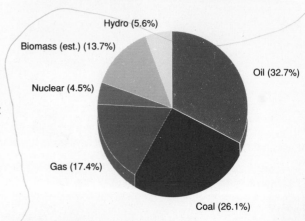

Figure 1.1: World energy use by fuel

Natural Energy Flows

The Sun

The Sun is a massive nuclear furnace radiating energy into space. One thousandth of a millionth of the Sun's output of around 400 000 000 000 000 000 000 000 000 watts is intercepted by the Earth. About 30 per cent of this energy is reflected back into space. The rest is absorbed by the atmosphere, land, and oceans, or in the evaporation, convection and precipitation of water.

Solar power

Solar collectors are widely used for domestic hot water in a number of countries. The highest concentration is in Japan, with over 1.5 million in Tokyo alone; there is also a very active market in Australia. Solar energy provides 3 per cent of primary energy use in Israel, where two thirds of homes have solar water heaters. The Israeli company, Luz, has installed nine solar power stations in California, the largest producing up to 80 MW [1] of power.

Photosynthesis

Sunlight is used by trees and other green plants to manufacture simple sugars (from carbon dioxide in the air and water in the soil) and to convert these into more complex organic molecules like starch, cellulose and lignin. This plant matter is called 'biomass'. When it is burnt, the Sun's energy is released as heat and light. The total amount of biomass on the surface of the Earth has an energy content equivalent to that of the world's proven fossil fuel reserves.

Biomass

Biomass currently provides about a seventh of the world's energy [2].

It accounts for over 40 per cent of all the fuel burnt in developing countries, and in some countries it provides over 90 per cent. It is the main fuel for about half the world's population, and the only source of energy for cooking for those in rural areas of the developing world. In India, the power from draught animals fed on biomass is estimated to be roughly comparable to the installed capacity of electric power (30,000 MW).

Biomass is also important in affluent Western countries. 4 per cent of the USA's energy comes from biomass - about the same as is generated by nuclear or hydro power. Canada and Sweden derive 8 per cent and 14 per cent respectively of their energy needs from biomass, mostly in the form of wood.

1. For explanations of this and other units of energy, see Boxes 2.1 and 2.2.
2. Scurlock and Hall, 1990

The Wind and the Waves

The energy in the wind and waves also comes from the sun. Differential heating of the planet's surface makes air move about the globe. This leads to regions of high and low air pressure and continual circulation in the atmosphere. When wind blows over water, energy is transferred and waves are produced.

Wind Power

More than 20,000 commercial-sized wind turbine generators [3] have been erected worldwide over the last decade, with an installed capacity in excess of 2,000 MW. Most are located in three separate areas of California, but Denmark has over 3,000 machines which, over the year, produce 1.5 per cent of the country's electricity. (In parts of Jutland, wind generates 40 per cent of the electricity annually.) It has been estimated that over one million wind pumps are in use worldwide, with an installed capacity of more than 1 GW.

Wave Power

Wave energy is currently being captured by experimental shore-based devices. On Islay, off the Scottish coast, a small prototype wave power plant was commissioned in 1991. Japan, India and China similarly have shore-based machines operating and one like the device on Islay is planned for Portugal.

Running Water

The Sun evaporates water from oceans and lakes and carries the vapour up and over the land. Cooling leads to condensation and precipitation which feeds mountain streams. The energy acquired when water is 'lifted' to higher ground is harnessed by hydroelectric installations. As water falls back to the sea it can turn turbines to generate electricity.

Hydroelectricity

Hydroelectric installations provide one fifth of the world's electricity and more than 40 per cent in developing countries. Current hydroelectric plants range from the very small ('micro' plants) to the very large, some of which can generate electricity equivalent to several large nuclear power stations. Water turbines can convert over 90 per cent of the energy available into useful power, and are amongst the most reliable and long-lived of all generation equipment. A well-maintained unit will last 50 years or more. For the UK, now that the 'capital costs' have been paid off, hydroelectricity provides the cheapest electricity in the country and generates just over 1 per cent of national electricity (in Scotland it provides over 10 per cent of the electricity generated).

3. Turbines of between 100 and 400 kW size.

Gravity

Gravitational pull from the moon, and to a lesser extent the sun, causes a tidal 'bulge' in the ocean, which moves as the planet spins on its axis. The bulge is only about one metre in mid ocean, but is amplified when the tidal flow is impeded by a continental shelf, or funnelled through straits or into bays and estuaries. The rise and fall of the tides follows a regular and entirely predictable pattern.

Tidal Power

Currently, tidal energy is not extensively used: the largest scheme (La Rance in France, left) generates up to 240 MW, and there are small barrages in Canada (20 MW) and the Soviet Union. In addition, China has over 250 small tidal pumping stations.

Heat from the Earth

'Geothermal' heat comes from the Earth's molten core and is enhanced in places by heat from the decay of naturally occurring radioactive elements. The temperature of the rock several kilometres below the Earth's surface is sufficiently high to raise steam for electricity generation.

Geothermal Energy

More than 20 countries are producing power from natural steam (totalling some 5,000 MW of capacity) and half a dozen more have harnessed geothermally heated water (about 12,000 MW in total) (right, a scheme in Paris). The Philippines already gets about 14 per cent of its electricity from geothermal steam. The world's largest geothermal field is in California. It is located about 70 miles north of San Francisco in the Mayacamas Mountains and is known as 'The Geysers'. The installed capacity of the complex is around 2,000 MW.

Old Energy, New Technology

Harnessing natural energy flows is not new. The Greeks and the Persians developed the principles of passive solar design 2,500 years ago. Windmills appeared around the same time and water-wheels a thousand years later. Tide mills were introduced by the Normans and were once common around the coast of southern England, France and Spain. Solar water heaters were being sold commercially in the US almost a century ago.

Modern technologies, however, can harness the same energy flows with far greater efficiency. Solar collectors now have special coatings which enable them to produce high temperatures, even when the sun is hidden behind cloud; photovoltaic solar cells which convert sunlight directly into electricity are based on advanced semiconductor technology; small hydroelectric power stations have electronic governors to maintain stable output and operate under remote control; and modern wind turbines make use of the latest composite materials and computer-aided design, and can anticipate and respond to changing wind behaviour.

Left: A traditional wind-driven mill. Right: MS3: A two bladed 300 kW wind turbine made by the Wind Energy Group. Each blade is 16.2 metres long and the tower is 25 metres in height. The turbine is set to 'cut-in' at windspeeds above 5 metres per second (m/s) and will automatically shut down at 25 m/s. It is designed to withstand windspeeds of up to 60 m/s (134 mph).

1.2 Why Renewables?

"Humanity is conducting an uncontrolled, globally pervasive experiment whose ultimate consequences could be second only to a global nuclear war. The Earth's atmosphere is being changed at an unprecedented rate by pollutants resulting from human activities, inefficient and wasteful fossil fuel use and the effects of a rapid population growth in many regions. These changes represent a major threat to international security and are already having harmful consequences over many parts of the globe."

Excerpt from the Toronto Statement, World Conference on *The Changing Atmosphere*, Toronto, June 1988

Energy Use and The Changing Atmosphere

Almost overnight, the threat of climate change due to pollution has become an issue of profound international concern. Today, the overwhelming consensus in the scientific community is that major, though largely unpredictable changes in climate are inevitable as a result of humanity releasing carbon dioxide and other 'greenhouse gases' into the atmosphere, mainly in the process of burning fossil fuels for energy.

The use of commercial energy has doubled over the last 25 years: fossil fuels equivalent to over 9,000 million tonnes of oil are now being extracted each year (equivalent to 50 of the largest supertankers full of oil each day). Energy consumption in the industrial West has largely stabilized; but overall, growth in global energy use continues at a rate of 2-3 per cent per year.

All energy technologies contribute directly or indirectly to global warming because fossil fuels are used in their manufacture. However, studies have shown that, per unit of electricity generated, the contribution from renewables is tiny compared with that from coal, oil and gas - and even nuclear power [4]. Furthermore, reducing emissions of methane (a potent greenhouse gas) from landfill sites by recycling and energy recovery can also help to reduce the threat of global warming.

The Greenhouse Effect and Climate Change

The Greenhouse Effect is a natural phenomenon which traps the sun's rays and helps keep the planet warm rather like the glass of a greenhouse. Without the Greenhouse Effect, life as we know it would not be possible. The effect is due to the presence of certain gases in the atmosphere which allow short wavelength sunlight through but prevent the longer wavelength thermal radiation from escaping. The most important natural 'greenhouse gases' are water vapour and carbon dioxide, although other gases (notably methane and nitrous oxide) also play a part. Of the key gases, carbon dioxide is the one we can most affect.

Over the last hundred years, mean global surface air temperatures have increased by around half a degree. Over the same time period, the emission of greenhouse gases has increased as a result of human activity and other gases, like chlorofluorocarbons (CFCs), which act powerfully to trap heat, have been introduced. Many scientists are now convinced that these two phenomena are linked. Global carbon dioxide levels are up 27 per cent on pre-industrial times and levels are now increasing by 0.5 per cent per annum. The levels of methane, nitrous oxide and CFCs are also increasing.

The Intergovernmental Panel on Climate Change (IPCC), set up by the United Nations in 1988 to assess the problem, has predicted that mean global temperatures could rise faster than in any period in the last 10,000 years and this will result in a rapid rise in sea level. Temperature swings will be more pronounced at the poles than the equator, leading to further melting of the polar ice.

The longer term consequences of changing global weather patterns include an increased frequency of violent storms, with flooding and coastal inundation, and in other places, drought, soil erosion and rapid desertification. Climate change will also affect food availability and trade, and will have an impact on virtually every other aspect of human activity. Millions may be forced to move home; many may die from virulent tropical diseases which are likely to spread more widely. Some animal and plant species will become extinct. Some low lying coastal areas will be lost. The changes are unlikely to be gradual, but may progress via a series of jumps.

---

4. Mortimer, 1990

The Implications

While there exists a scientific consensus that the climate is changing as a result of human activity, there remains considerable uncertainty about just how rapidly the climate will change and what the precise implications are likely to be. Understanding climatic change is an enormously complex issue and the computer models used to make the predictions are still relatively crude. However, four conclusions are clear:

■ energy production and use is responsible for over half of greenhouse gas emissions (see Figure 1.2);

■ two thirds of the annual human-made environmental release of carbon dioxide (around 5.7 billion tonnes of carbon per year +/- 10 per cent) is being emitted by just 12 nations;

■ unless action is taken to reduce the emission of greenhouse gases we are likely to see a significant increase in planetary temperatures, climatic change and a rise in sea levels;

■ the rich nations must act first to reduce their consumption of fossil fuels by cutting out energy wastage and by increasing use of renewable energy.

Figure 1.2: Contributions by sector to the Greenhouse Effect as a result of human activity [5]

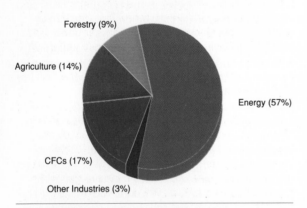

Forestry (9%)

Agriculture (14%)

Energy (57%)

CFCs (17%)

Other Industries (3%)

5. Lashof and Tirpak, 1989; IPCC, 1990
6. Clark 1990
7. AEA Technology, 1991
8. Yuri Shcherbak, Vice Chairman of the Supreme Soviet's Commission on Environment and Nuclear Energy, 1990.

"Taking into consideration that the ECE region [the industrialised world] *presently accounts for about 70% of global primary energy and fossil fuel use, we assume a major responsibility to limit or reduce greenhouse gases and other emissions and to lead a global effort to address this matter by promoting energy efficiency, energy conservation and the use of environmentally sound and renewable energy sources."*

Bergen Ministerial Declaration on Sustainable Development in the Economic Commission for Europe Region, Signed by UK Government, Bergen 16th May 1990.

Inevitable Outcomes

Disasters involving nuclear and fossil fuel sources cannot be avoided and can have catastrophic implications:

■ As a result of the explosion in the core of the Chernobyl nuclear reactor on 26 April 1986, harmful radioactivity spread over large parts of Europe. Thirty one people died as a result of the initial explosion and it is estimated that 40,000 more people may die worldwide as a result of the radiation exposure following the explosion [7]. Some 116,000 people have so far been evacuated from their homes, and the levels of contamination in Byelorussia, the Ukraine and the Russian Republic are forcing the evacuation of over 200,000 more people. The Soviet Union has put the total economic cost of the disaster at 200 billion roubles (this was equivalent to roughly £200 billion at the time when the statement was made) [8].

■ Every year there are thousands of incidents world-wide involving oil spills from tankers, oil rigs and oil storage facilities. Between 1970 and 1985, there were 186 separate major oil spills, each involving more than 1,300 tonnes of oil. In 1989 the Exxon Valdez ran aground off Alaska causing America's worst oil accident. 39,000 tonnes of oil formed a slick covering over 1,600 square miles, badly affecting wildlife in the region.

In addition, the process of burning coal itself is a major cause of acid rain which has seriously damaged forests and lakes in North America and Northern and Eastern Europe.

Figure 1.3: Carbon dioxide emissions for 12 selected countries [6]

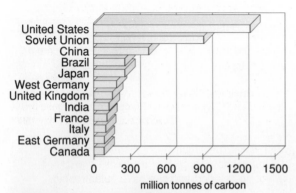

1. Current annual carbon dioxide release.

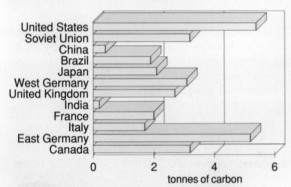

2. Current annual carbon dioxide release per person

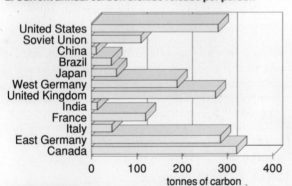

3. Cumulative historic carbon dioxide emissions per person (1860 - 1986)

9. British Petroleum, 1990
10. International Energy Agency, 1990
11. Organisation for Economic Cooperation and Development, 1988

Global dependence on dwindling fossil fuel resources, like petroleum, results in heightened political tension, instability and war. 65 per cent of proven oil reserves are located in the Middle East [9].

The International Energy Agency has forecast that while the UK exported 22 million tonnes of oil equivalent in 1988, it will need to finance net energy imports of 45 million tonnes per year by the year 2000 [10].

Renewable Benefits

Compared with technologies currently in use, those that harness the sun, the wind and other natural energy flows are relatively benign [11]. Together, they provide a diverse, secure and inexhaustible source of energy and one which cannot easily be 'turned off' by some foreign power. The very diversity of sources, the small size of many of the technologies and the short time it takes to build them, offers greater flexibility in planning - especially in the electricity supply sector where conventional power plant can take ten years or more to plan and construct. Small units, generating electricity locally, also reduce fuel transport costs and transmission losses, can strengthen the electricity grid and can improve the reliability of supply by reducing dependence on fossil fuels.

Most importantly, coupled with a programme of improved energy efficiency, renewable energy can begin to displace fossil fuels and nuclear power and thus help reduce the risks to the environment from acid rain, the accumulation of nuclear waste, the threat of nuclear accidents, nuclear weapons proliferation and climate change.

The benefits of renewable sources of energy extend further than just the production of relatively clean heat and power. Most also provide other useful services; for example, treating sewage or farm-yard manure in a digester generates methane gas which can be used as a fuel, as well as reducing the pollution potential of the slurry.

Finally, renewable energy is popular: according to opinion polls and surveys, people give renewable energy a far higher rating than 'dirty' fossil fuels or 'unsafe' nuclear power.

Renewables: Diverse, natural, indigenous, inexhaustible, relatively clean and relatively safe.

Solar power in the deserts of southern California: Rows of large parabolic mirrors focus sunlight onto a heat-collection element, heating oil to around 350°C. The oil is pumped through a central heat exchanger, generating steam which drives a turbo-generator. Electronic sensors adjust the mirrors' position to keep the sun continually in focus.

1.3 The Potential for Renewable Energy in the UK

The theoretical potential for renewable energy varies from country to country. The UK is particularly favoured, although it has hardly begun to make use of this natural wealth - it currently generates just 2 per cent of its electricity from renewable energy. The country's wind resources (on and off-shore) are amongst the best in the world. There are also large quantities of wastes and residues, such as refuse and straw, that could be used as fuel, and there is potential for growing trees and other energy crops.

The UK also has considerable potential for harnessing the waves and the tides and tapping geothermal heat. In addition, despite the country's northern latitude, there are opportunities for making better use of the Sun through more carefully designed buildings, solar collectors and photovoltaic arrays (which convert sunlight directly into electricity) - incidental solar gains through windows and walls already account for some 15 per cent of the energy used in dwellings [12].

It is possible to cut the UK's dependence on fossil fuels by as much as a half, over the next 30-40 years through a combination of cost-effective energy efficiency improvements and low impact renewable energy technologies.

Nuclear Power

Nuclear power does not feature in the energy path proposed here. It does not produce more than about 6 per cent of the UK's total energy use and is currently declining in importance. After more than thirty years of 'commercial' operation and in spite of significant injections of public money, the UK nuclear industry has failed to produce economic electricity, and failed to find an acceptable management plan for dealing with radioactive waste and old reactors.

While nuclear proponents claim that nuclear power has a role in helping to reduce the carbon dioxide emissions causing climate change, they offer no convincing justification for replacing one environmental risk with another. Moreover, the nuclear industry has yet to answer adequately the claims that massive cuts can be made in emissions using cheaper and less environmentally damaging technologies than nuclear power. (See bibliography for further reading.)

The remainder of the book looks at how this might be achieved: Chapter 2 explains how energy is used in the UK and where it is wasted; Chapter 3 describes a number of renewable energy technologies, identifies those which are most appropriate for the UK and shows what contribution renewable energy could make; Chapter 4 shows how renewables might complement other energy policy developments; and Chapter 5 analyses the measures that will need to be taken, such as the setting up of a new Renewable Energy Agency, to overcome the many obstacles that renewables face. As this book will show, the main barriers to achieving a cut in fossil fuels and greater use of renewables are not technical, but political and institutional.

One of the main objectives of the book is to demonstrate that modern renewable energy technologies represent the most practical and appropriate tools for conserving resources and helping to combat global pollution.

---

12. Henderson *et al*, 1990

2. Energy Use in the UK

This chapter analyses energy use in the UK. It uses the internationally recognised unit of energy, the joule (J). How the joule relates to more familiar energy units is explained in boxes 2.1 and 2.2.

Production

Since 1980, the UK has been virtually self-sufficient in energy, largely as a result of exploiting its indigenous deposits of coal, oil and gas. However, some coal and natural gas continue to be imported, along with a small amount of electricity from France, and 'light' North Sea oil is exchanged for 'heavy' Middle-Eastern crude. The only fuel that is currently imported in any significant quantity is uranium for the nuclear programme - there is no indigenous production of uranium in the UK, and little prospect of it.

Proven UK reserves of oil (put at 500 million tonnes) are estimated to last just 5.5 years at current rates of consumption and proved reserves of gas, 0.6 trillion cubic metres, about 13 years [13]. The UK's coal reserves are considerably greater (9,200 million tonnes), but even these would be nearing exhaustion in less than a century at current extraction rates. These figures are likely to be pessimistic. Historically, the level of reserves has tended to increase as new finds have been made and extraction techniques improved. Moreover, the size of the reserves is directly linked to the price of energy: as fuel prices rise it becomes worthwhile to exploit more marginal fields. Nevertheless, the UK can be expected to resume importing oil after the turn of the century, and gas not long after.

Box 2.1 Definitions

Energy Terms:
■ **Primary energy** is the heat content of any fuel before it is processed and transmitted to the consumer.

■ Some energy is 'lost' (as heat) when primary energy is processed and transmitted. **Delivered** energy is the energy that is supplied to (and paid for by) the consumer.

■ Further energy losses occur when the delivered energy is used - such as in an appliance or machine. **End-use energy** is the energy that is actually available to the consumer as heat, for example, or light.

■ **Power** is the rate at which energy is supplied or used.

Energy Measurements:
■ Primary energy is often measured in **millions of tonnes of oil or coal** (Mto and Mtc) or their equivalent (Mtoe and Mtce). These are rather imprecise terms since the heat content of oil and coal varies.

■ By contrast, **the joule** (J) is precisely defined, and is an internationally recognised unit of energy measurement. For example, lifting a kilo bag of sugar its own height requires about 1 joule. It is, however, a rather small unit: there are 44 million billion joules in one Mtoe.

■ Gas is usually measured in **therms** (Th) or cubic metres: 400 million therms, or 1,100 million cubic metres of natural gas are equivalent to 1 Mto. One therm will run an average gas fire for 4 hours, and will cost around 42 pence (1991) [14].

■ Power is measured in **watts** (W). A watt is a joule per second. Commercially-sized wind turbines, for example, have power ratings ranging from about 50 kilowatts (kW) to 400 kW; a large power station has a power output from about 500 to 2,000 megawatts (MW) (see box 2.2).

■ Electrical energy is more usually measured in units of **kilowatt-hours** (kWh), where one kWh is the energy used by a one-kilowatt device (for example a one-bar electric fire) in one hour. One kWh equals 3,600,000 joules and costs around 7 pence (1991).

---

13. British Petroleum, 1990
14. Figures based on a 25,000 Btu gas fire.

Box 2.2 Conversion Factors

Joules:
1,000 J = 1 kilojoule (kJ)
1,000 kJ = 1 megajoule (MJ)
1,000 MJ = 1 gigajoule (GJ)
1,000 GJ = 1 terajoule (TJ)
1,000 TJ = 1 petajoule (PJ)

44 GJ equivalent to
   - 1 tonne of oil
   - roughly 1.7 tonnes of coal
   - 1,100 cubic metres of natural gas
   - 400 therms of natural gas
44 PJ equivalent to 1 million tonnes of oil

Watts:
1,000 W = 1 kilowatt (kW)
1,000 kW = 1 megawatt (MW)
1,000 MW = 1 gigawatt (GW)
1,000 GW = 1 terawatt (TW)
1,000 TW = 1 petawatt (PW)

Everyday Energy Measures:
1 kWh = one electricity "unit" = 3.6 MJ
1 therm (often used for natural gas) = 106 MJ
1 British Thermal Unit (Btu) = 1.06 kJ
1 gallon of petrol = 159 MJ
1 litre of petrol = 35 MJ

Use

For the last few years, the UK has been using energy at the rate of around 9,000 Petajoules (PJ) per year, equivalent to more than 900 gallons of oil for every man, woman and child in the country (see Figure 2.1). The UK comes seventh in the global league table of major energy users after the United States, the Soviet Union, China, Japan, Germany and Canada.

One quarter of the world's population uses energy at over six times the rate of the other three quarters [16]. In poor countries people have no choice but to rely on traditional fuels such as wood, charcoal, and animal dung for their cooking, heating and lighting, and will continue to do so as their population expands.

Following the Second World War, total energy use in the UK increased dramatically. The main contributory factors were the unprecedented growth in electricity use and private transport and the widespread introduction of domestic central heating. Primary energy use reached its peak in 1973 (9330 PJ/yr), then fell back following the quadrupling of oil prices in the wake of the first oil crisis. Demand bottomed out in 1982 and has been rising gradually ever since (see Figure 2.2).

Figure 2.1: Per capita primary energy use for 4 nations for years 1960, 1973 and 1986 [15]

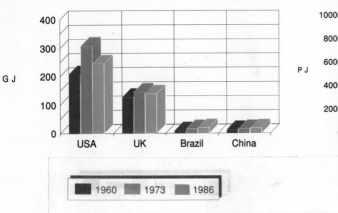

Figure 2.2: UK inland use of primary energy by fuel from 1950 to 1990 [17]

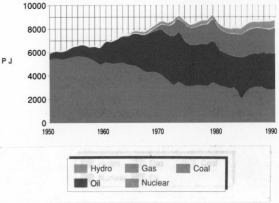

15. United Nations, 1965; 1981; 1986
16. Scurlock and Hall, 1990, estimate that the respective energy consumption figures are 220 GJ/yr and 36 GJ/yr.
17. Department of Energy, 1990

In 1950, coal provided 86 per cent of the UK's primary energy. Since then, its market share has fallen away as the country has switched to oil and gas. The main market for coal today is the electricity supply industry, although even this market is currently facing competition from the use of natural gas in electricity generation.

In 1990, oil and gas provided almost 60 per cent of total energy, and coal most of the remainder, with nuclear power and hydro-electricity making up the balance. This cost the country £42 billion, 8 per cent of the Gross Domestic Product (GDP). Average expenditure on energy per household was around £20 per week.

Waste

The rate at which an advanced industrial country like the UK uses primary energy says very little about how much energy actually reaches the customer and is usefully converted into heat, light, transportation or useful work ('end-use energy'). This is a critical question since consumer satisfaction is measured not by *how much* energy is used but on the *quality* of the service provided (for example, heat, light and refrigeration). People want these services, not the energy itself. Many of these services can be provided using far less energy than is currently the case (see Chapter 4). An analysis of how energy is used in the UK reveals that much of it is wasted in draughty and badly insulated buildings, poorly designed appliances, 'gas-guzzling' vehicles and inefficient industrial processes.

30 per cent of the energy value of primary fuels is currently lost as waste heat during conversion to electricity and premium fuels (such as heating oil and petrol, piped and bottled gas, and coke) [18] and the transmission and distribution of these forms of energy to the final consumers. More losses occur when this energy is used to provide services - warmth, hot water, light, cooked food. These may amount to a further 25-30 per cent, as illustrated in the flow diagram (see Figure 2.3).

Around two thirds of the fuel and electricity purchased by consumers is actually used to supply heat, and more than half of this is used at temperatures below the boiling point of water. One quarter of all energy used in the UK is in the form of liquid fuel for transport. Less than 10 per cent of end uses - lighting, television, motors and appliances, welding and electrochemistry, communications and electronics - specifically requires energy in the form of electricity. This is shown by the breakdown by end-use presented in Figure 2.4 over. Figure 2.5 (over) shows how energy is supplied for each sector.

---

18. During conversion into electricity up to 60 per cent of the primary energy value can be lost as waste heat.

Figure 2.3: Sankey diagram: Current UK energy use

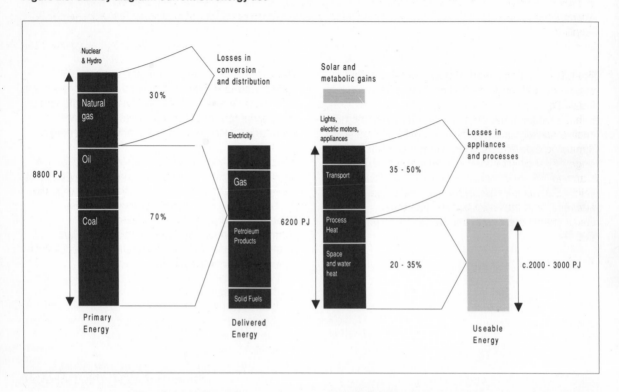

Figure 2.4: Analysis of UK energy use by major applications [19]

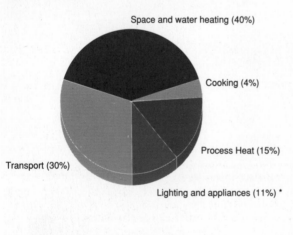

Figure 2.5: Final energy use in the UK for each sector [20]

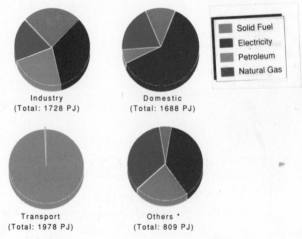

19. Department of Energy, 1990
20. Department of Energy, 1990

* Mainly agriculture, public administration and commerce

3. Renewable Energy for the UK

"The shopping list for fuel and electricity supply technologies is already long, and growing longer. We can pick and choose from a wide variety of innovative options already known to be technically feasible, with environmental impacts that may be significantly more acceptable than those of traditional fuel and electricity supplies."

Walter Patterson, *The Energy Alternative*, 1990.

The UK is well-endowed with renewable energy resources both on and off-shore. The challenge is to find ways to capture these resources; ways which are both convenient and economical, and which do not involve socially unacceptable or environmentally damaging side-effects. This chapter describes the range of renewable energy systems available and examines their potential for the UK. Two boxes, which discuss the use of the term "technical potential" and the issue of how economic assessments are made, can be found on pages 18 and 19.

The two resources that can make the biggest contribution to meeting UK energy needs in the short to medium term are wind and biomass. In the longer term, a number of other resources could become important, including solar, tidal, and wave energy.

It is possible that renewable energy could supply a quarter to a third of the UK's primary energy by 2020, provided that measures are taken to cut energy use through energy efficiency improvements (see Chapter 4). To push the renewable energy contribution above this level by this date might involve profound shifts in lifestyle and have significant environmental implications.

It is possible that, during the next century, the UK could be exporting wind generated electricity in the winter months while, in the summer, importing electricity generated from geothermal steam (above) and hydro in Iceland, from wood grown in Scandanavia or from solar power stations operating in Spain. At high voltages energy can be moved relatively efficiently.

Box 3.1 'Technical Potential'

The assessment of the technical potential for different renewable energy systems is an essential prerequisite for strategic planning. However, such studies should not obscure the need for action based on what we already know of the wealth of renewable energy in the UK. The UK is so far from realising even the lowest estimates made of the technical potential for any renewable technology (other than large-scale hydroelectricity), that "upper limits" are currently somewhat academic.

The technical potential of a resource is not an absolute figure; its assessment involves making assumptions about the technology that is used to harness the resource and about economic and social factors that may constrain its deployment.

The potential for wind energy, for example, involves assumptions about wind speeds, topography, the size and spacing of turbines, land (or sea) availability, machine performance and restrictions imposed on siting. The technical potential of hot dry rock geothermal involves assumptions concerning temperature gradients in the rock, the depths of wells, the behaviour of the water reservoir, the thermodynamics of converting heat into electricity, and the energy requirements for operating the pumping systems.

Moreover, changes in climate, as a result of global warming, may well affect the potential for renewable energy: they could alter levels of cloud cover and rainfall, and hence the performance of solar collectors, and the growth rate of trees and other energy crops. The country's wind and wave resources could also be significantly affected.

Estimates of 'technical potential' should therefore only be used as a rough guide to resource availability. In practice,

rather than analyse and argue about the fine tuning of resource estimates, it is more constructive to look at what would be required to meet a particular level of demand from a particular resource. The more one is prepared to pay, and the greater the intrusion one is prepared to put up with, the larger the resource that can be tapped. This can be shown graphically in a 'resource cost diagram' (see Figure 3.1).

Figure 3.1: Resource cost curve for all renewable energy sources in North Western area [21]

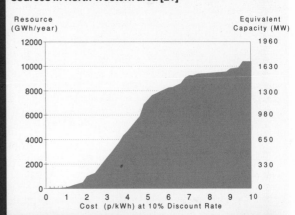

However, such assessments must be treated with caution since they depend on the economic assumptions used and give no credit for the environmental benefits of renewable energy.

In the last analysis, and within the constraints of what is technically possible, the amount of energy which is obtained from renewable sources is a matter of choice.

21. NORWEB, 1989

Box 3.2 Economics

It is important to make some assessment of the economics of renewable energy technologies to guide decisions on the allocation of resources. Yet for any technology, particularly new ones, such an exercise is fraught with difficulty. Numerous factors affect costs both now and in the future. In the end, whether a project is deemed worthwhile depends on what assumptions are made about these factors in the economic calculation.

Critical to the economics of any particular renewable energy project are the nature and characteristics of the energy resource at the particular planned site. A water turbine operating on a site with a high head of water will produce electricity far more cheaply than a similar machine on a different site operating at a lower head. Without site-specific data, many assumptions have to be made about the resource.

Significant assumptions have also to be made about the future performance of current technologies. Some economic assessments are based upon experience gained to date from prototypes and include development and launch costs. Others consider future improvements in performance, availability and operating life, and take account of the possible reductions in costs brought about by technical developments and mass production. These two methods can end up producing very different results.

Renewable energy technologies tend to be seen as expensive because extensive structures are usually required to capture and convert significant amounts of energy into a useful form. On the other hand, there are obviously no fuel costs for most systems, and the cost of operating and maintaining plant is not usually very high - for wind turbines, for example, it could be 2-3 per cent of initial capital costs per year. Other costs include local taxes, insurance contributions, and the cost of servicing the capital loan. The fact that most renewable energy technologies can be installed rapidly means little or no interest to pay on the loan during construction. (Large tidal barrages are an exception.)

The revenue from sales of electricity or heat depends on the quality and consistency of the output and the time it is delivered. Utilities will pay most for electricity generated at times of peak demand because this is when they use plant from lower down the "merit order". (Generating plant is brought on line progressively as the demand grows, starting with the lowest cost plant). What utilities are prepared to pay will also depend on whether the equipment can provide intermittent supply (which makes savings simply by displacing fossil fuels burnt in other plant) or firm power (which also saves expenditure on building or operating other plant).

The choice of "discount rate" (the rate at which the value of money is assumed to depreciate) is critical to the economic viability of new plant: high discount rates (15-20 per cent) may indicate unit generation costs 4 - 6 times higher than for low discount rates (5 per cent). Higher discount rates are usually applied to privately funded projects using new and untried technologies. Virtually all of the UK's existing power stations were built using state funding to which low discount rates applied, making them appear cheaper. The effect of discount rates on wind power costs can be seen from the example in Figure 3.2.

Figure 3.2: Variation in wind power generation costs for different recovery periods and different discount rates [22]

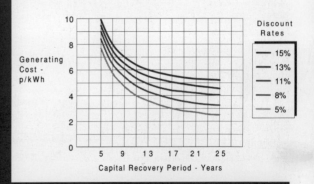

In view of all these factors, this report does not attempt to give precise assessments of costs for individual technologies. Instead it provides some approximation of relative costs under current economic conditions. As explained in Section 5.1, the conventional approach to economic assessment fails to take account of the environmental benefits of renewable energy and until these are calculated and included in the equation, any economic analysis will necessarily be incomplete.

22. Laughton, 1990

3.1 Wind Power

More than 20,000 commercial-sized wind turbines have been erected worldwide over the last decade, with an installed capacity of more than 2,000 MW. About 80 per cent of the machines are located in three separate regions in California. These already supply 1 per cent of the state's electricity, enough to serve the residential needs of a city of over 900,000 people - more than the population of San Francisco.

Today, ten years on from the first commercial developments in wind energy, turbine performance and reliability have dramatically improved and costs have fallen considerably. In California, the well-publicised problems that dogged many of the early machines have now been sorted out and machines are operating for more than 95 per cent of the time (better than modern combustion plant). Though federal tax credits were used initially to encourage the development of California's wind industry, nearly half of today's wind generating capacity has been installed without the use of such credits.

Figure 3.3: European Wind Atlas [23]

The UK Potential

The UK's wind resources are amongst the best in the world. One EC-sponsored study has estimated the size of the accessible European wind resource at over 4,000 TWh per year, some two and a half times the electricity currently used by the European Community's 12 Member States [24]. More than one third of this potential (1,760 TWh/y) is in the UK.

Another study, which used more modest assumptions about machine performance and siting, put the available resource for the UK at 760 TWh per year, three times current UK electricity use [25]. In 1990, the Department of Energy itself published an assessment of the UK wind energy resource, which took into account physical, institutional and environmental constraints. The assessment concluded that approximately 122 TWh per year of electricity could, in principle, be generated, equal to almost 50 per cent of annual UK electricity consumption [26]. This assumed that turbines could be sited on the 12 per cent of UK land area found to be 'unconstrained'. However, as Figure 3.4 shows, UK plans to harness the wind have been delayed. This was caused by pessimistic early assessments of the potential, and by major institutional and financial constraints.

Wind speeds at 50 metres above ground level for four different topographic conditions

	Open Plain	At a sea coast	Open sea	Hills and ridges
	m/s	m/s	m/s	m/s
	> 7.5	> 8.5	> 9.0	> 11.5
	6.5 - 7.5	7.0 - 8.5	8.0 - 9.0	10.0 - 11.5
	5.5 - 6.5	6.0 - 7.0	7.0 - 8.0	8.5 - 10.0
	4.5 - 5.5	5.0 - 6.0	5.5 - 7.0	7.0 - 8.5
	< 4.5	< 5.0	< 5.5	< 7.0

23. Commission of European Communities, 1989
24. Selzer, 1989

25. Grubb, 1988
26. Energy Technology Support Unit / Institute of Terrestrial Ecology, 1990

Country/State	Installed Capacity to date	Wind Energy Target
California	1,400 MW	10% of electricity supply by 2000
Denmark	250 MW	1600-1800 MW by 2000
Holland	100 MW	1000 MW by 2000
India	35 MW	5,000 MW by 2000
Germany	35 MW	250 MW by 1995
United Kingdom	8 MW	No wind energy target

Figure 3.4: Wind Energy Installed Capacities and Targets (MW) for Various Countries

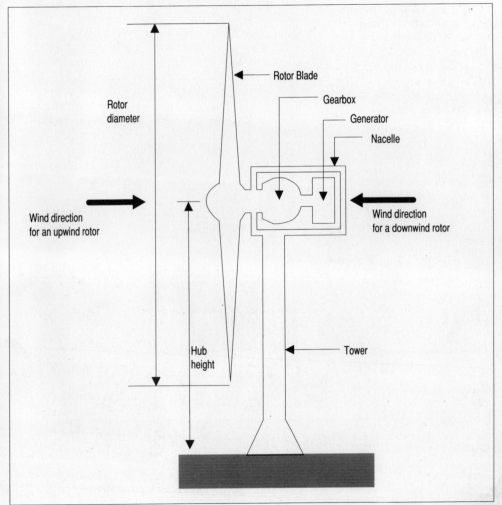

Figure 3.5: Cross sectional diagram of horizontal-axis wind turbine

Figure 3.6: Map of main proposed and existing wind energy developments in the UK (as of 1 May, 1991)

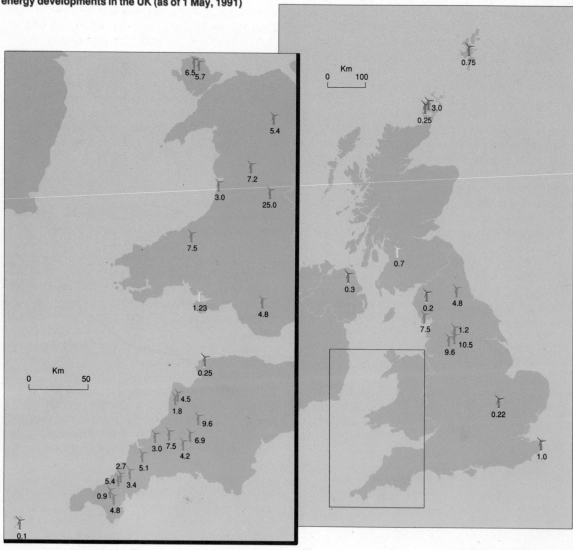

Key

Y   Single turbine: existing (as of 1/5/1991)

Development comprising a number of turbines:
existing (as of 1/5/1991)

Development comprising a number of turbines:
proposed (as of 1/5/1991)

Capacity of each development measured in megawatts (MW)

Within the last decade, the size-range favoured by utilities in Denmark has increased from around 60 kW to around 200 kW, and there is now growing interest in machines of 450 kW. The majority of these commercial machines have two or three blades which rotate about a horizontal shaft sweeping an area 20 to 30 metres across. Larger machines (up to 4 MW), with blades up to 90 metres across, have been erected, but these are still experimental.

There is some interest in developing vertical axis machines. Vertical axis machines have two distinct advantages: they do not need equipment to turn the rotor into the wind and they are less subject to gravity-induced stress fatigue (which is a major consideration in big horizontal axis machines). However, there are problems in trying to achieve a steady output because each blade continually passes through the other's shadow.

Based on information from 128 wind turbines in Denmark (each 95 kW), it has been calculated that it takes just 100 days (1.4 per cent of its lifetime production) for each turbine to pay back the energy costs used in its own construction [27].

Land

The amount of land actually used by the wind turbines themselves, the turbine base, the foundations and the access roads is less than 1 per cent of the total area covered by the wind farm. The rest of the area can still be used for agricultural purposes, for crops or for grazing. The land used is therefore little more than conventional energy systems of equivalent output, especially if land use for coal or uranium mines is considered [28].

Noise

Noise is not normally an issue with well designed machines except at very low wind speeds, and then only for near neighbours. Potential noise disturbance can be eliminated by careful siting, modifying the operational regime or fitting additional acoustic insulation [29].

27. WindStats Newsletter, 1990
28. Windirection, 1988
29. Rand, 1990
30. For guidelines on windfarm siting, see Clarke, 1988; Taylor, Rand and Larke, 1990; and, Rand, 1990
31. Walker, 1988

Siting

As wind turbines become more commercially available, special attention needs to be given to their siting: the two principal issues relate to noise and visual intrusion on the landscape (see also Section 5.3).

The potential for developing wind energy in the UK will be marred by insensitive development, unless developers recognise the crucial importance of careful siting [30]. Developing the potential for off-shore wind energy will be largely free from such constraints, though the technical challenge will be greater.

Off-shore Wind

The UK's off-shore wind resource is potentially very large, even after allowance is made for areas that may be excluded because of possible interference with shipping or fishing, or because of unsuitable seabed conditions. An investigation of the UK's off-shore wind resource, carried out by the Central Electricity Generating Board [31], put the gross resource around the British Isles at around 240 TWh per year (85 per cent of total annual UK electricity use) and suggested that more than half of this (134 TWh per year) was usable.

The wind tends to be stronger off-shore and less turbulent, but construction and operating costs are considerably higher. Large scale deployment of off-shore wind turbines could be emerging before the year 2000 given an appropriate level of funding.

An off-shore scheme was proposed for the UK involving the construction of a 750 kW turbine off the Norfolk Coast. This project has been postponed because of problems with the contract. Abroad, a number of wind turbines have already been erected in coastal locations or in shallow off-shore waters. Denmark is building the world's first off-shore wind farm off Lolland Island, south of Copenhagen. It consists of eleven 450 kW machines up to 3 km off the coast in 2.5 - 5 metres of water. Denmark has already accumulated considerable experience in operating wind turbines in a salt-laden marine environment. Sixteen machines built out along a breakwater in Ebeltoft harbour near Aarhus have been operating since 1985.

Sweden's first off-shore wind turbine was put in place in 1990. The 220 kW, 28 metre diameter machine is mounted on a tripod in five metres of water 250 metres off the coast North East of Malmo. It is essentially a standard machine, uprated for the more hostile environment.

A Programme for the UK

The UK should aim to have at least 2,500 MW of installed wind energy capacity in operation by 2005, and 22,000 MW by 2020, with possibly half of the installed capacity off-shore by the latter date. A programme of this size would deliver around 60 TWh per year of electricity by 2020, equivalent to over 20 per cent of the UK's annual electricity use.

To date, the Department of Energy has spent £46 million (in 1990 money) over 12 years in support of wind energy in the UK through the Government's research and development programme. Though on-shore projects are starting to emerge, underlying research and demonstration is still needed for further refinement, for off-shore development and for issues such as system integration and technical harmonisation. For these areas, the wind energy research budget should at least be doubled so that it can include a detailed study of the off-shore wind resource, the costs of an off-shore demonstration programme, and support for encouraging the domestic manufacturing potential and the development of wind energy in the agricultural markets.

Above: Denmark's largest wind farm is at Velling in the West of Jutland. It has 100 wind turbines and a capacity of about 13 MW. The land is farmed right up to the base of the machines.

Top: Ebeltoft harbour, Denmark.
Right: The experimental I MW wind turbine generator at Richborough in Kent is expected to generate more 2000 MWh per year of electricity. The tower is 45 metres high, and each blade about 27 metres long. The blades have variable pitch tips for aerodynamic control.
Above: Construction of the world's first off-shore wind farm, off Lolland Island, Denmark.

Wind Summary Box:

1. Possible future contribution from renewable energy, identifying contribution from wind power.

a) As Primary Energy Equivalent **b) As Electricity**

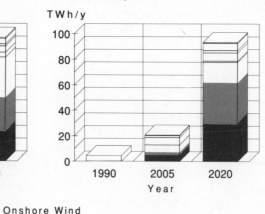

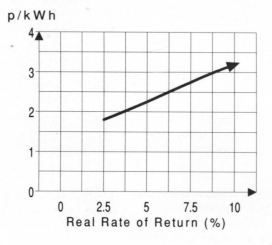

**2. Generation Cost
[Source: Laughton, 1990]**

3. UK Research and Development Budget (in 1990-91 prices) [Source: Hansard, 10 July 1989]

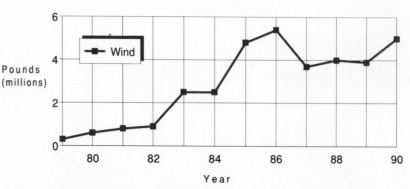

3.2 Biomass

It has been estimated that 250 million tonnes of organic waste matter are generated in the UK each year. This includes the organic component of municipal refuse, old car tyres, agricultural and forestry residues, pig slurry, rotting vegetables and a host of other unsavoury wastes. Much of this material is simply thrown away, often incurring considerable disposal costs. More than 90 per cent of municipal solid waste - around 22 million tonnes per year - is disposed of to landfill, with most of the rest incinerated without heat recovery (recycling schemes currently recover about 2 per cent of paper, glass and ferrous and non-ferrous metals in domestic refuse). Crop residues tend to be burnt in the field, and forestry residues left to rot.

Premium Fuels

Biomass - either wastes or crops grown specifically for use as fuel - can displace fossil fuels and reduce greenhouse gas and other polluting emissions. Though carbon dioxide is released when organic matter is burnt, it is absorbed again when new plant matter is grown - there need therefore be no net release of carbon dioxide in well-managed systems. Biomass can be burnt directly or converted into premium solid, liquid or gaseous fuels suitable for existing furnaces and boilers, or for use in internal combustion engines. Such refined 'biofuels' have calorific values comparable with conventional fuels and can be stored for long periods without deterioration.

A wide variety of technologies for converting biomass are available (see Box 3.3) and in principle, any feedstock can be treated in a number of ways. Domestic refuse, wood waste and straw can be burnt directly to provide heat and electricity, or converted into a low calorific value gas by 'pyrolysis'. Alternatively, they can also be broken down mechanically or chemically and digested to generate 'biogas' (a combustible mixture of methane and carbon dioxide).

Box 3.3 Examples of Conversion Technologies

Dry Processes

Combustion: The technology of direct combustion is well understood, straightforward and commercially available. Combustion systems come in a wide range of shapes and sizes burning virtually any kind of fuel, from chicken manure and straw bales to tree trunks, municipal refuse and scrap tyres. Some of the ways in which heat from burning wastes is currently used include space and water heating, industrial processing and electricity generation.

Pyrolysis: A wide range of energy-rich fuels can be produced by roasting dry woody matter like straw and woodchips. The process has been used for centuries to produce charcoal. The material is pulverised or shredded then fed into a reactor vessel and heated in the absence of air. Pyrolysis can also be carried out in the presence of a small quantity of oxygen ('gasification'), water ('steam gasification') or hydrogen ('hydrogenation'). One of the most useful products is methane, which is a suitable fuel for electricity generation using high-efficiency gas turbines.

Wet Processes

Anaerobic Digestion: Biogas is produced when wet sewage sludge, animal dung or green plants are allowed to decompose in a sealed tank under anaerobic (oxygen-free) conditions. Feedstocks like wood shavings, straw and refuse may be used, but digestion takes much longer. Each kilogram of organic material (dry weight) can be expected to yield 450-500 litres of biogas (9-12 MJ). The residue left after digestion is a potentially valuable fertilizer or compost.

Fermentation: Ethanol (ethyl alcohol) is produced by the fermentation of sugar solution by natural yeasts. Suitable feedstocks include crushed sugar beet and fruit. Sugars can also be manufactured from vegetable starches and cellulose by pulping and cooking, or from cellulose by milling and treatment with hot acid. After about 30 hours of fermentation, the brew contains 6-10 per cent alcohol, which can be removed by distillation and used as a fuel.

The most efficient way of getting energy from dry biomass is by burning it, or converting it to another form of solid fuel, like refined waste derived fuel. Wet biomass, like sewage sludge and vegetable wastes, can also be dried and burnt, but considerable amounts of energy are required to drive off moisture. This diminishes the net energy value of the biomass. A better option is to use digestion or fermentation processes. While the conversion efficiencies with such processes tend to be considerably lower than with combustion, the fuels produced have higher value and wider application.

Waste Combustion

Straw

Straw is widely used as a fuel on farms on the Continent; there are estimated to be some 12,000 small straw burners in Denmark alone, which along with some 30 or so straw-fired district heating schemes, supply 1.5 per cent of national energy needs. However, straw is bulky, which means that storage can be a problem. Large straw-burning furnaces are gradually being accepted, for example, amongst horticulturists, and for steam-raising in rural industry. A 5 MW generator would burn 47,000 tonnes of straw in a year and produce 37 million kWh of electricity.

An estimated 165,000 tonnes of straw are currently being burnt in the UK each year to provide space and water-heating and heat for agricultural or industrial purposes. This, however, represents only a small fraction of the potential. Over 40 per cent of the straw produced annually, with an energy content equivalent to 1 per cent of UK primary energy use (some 6.6 million tonnes), is either burnt in the field or ploughed in. Recent environmental legislation to ban burning in the field may provide the impetus for increased utilisation [32].

Wood waste

Dry sawdust and offcuts produced during the processing of cut timber make very good fuel: 35,000 tonnes, one third of current production, are estimated to be used each year by the British furniture industry to provide space and water-heating and process heat. When wood is used as a fuel, there are low suphur and nitrogen oxide emissions, but, there is concern about the by-products of using pesticide treated materials (as with straw). There is some potential to use more wood waste, especially residues arising from forestry operations. This could be collected, dried and used by rural industry.

The technology for burning wood waste is well tried and tested. One manufacturing company in Denmark, Junkers Industries, has recently installed a large waste wood boiler at its main timber yard at Koge, 25 miles south of Copenhagen. The boiler consumes 14 tonnes of wood waste an hour and produces 60 tonnes of steam for use in the factory and 9.4 MW of power. In the USA, about 8,000 MW is generated by burning wood and agricultural residues.

Refuse

Refuse incineration is primarily a waste management process which seeks to harness the valuable energy content of waste products through combustion. The heat derived from incineration can be used both for district heating and for electricity generation. Almost 350 energy-from-refuse incinerators are now in operation, mostly on the Continent and in Japan. There are about 37 refuse incinerators operating in the UK, but only a handful provide useful energy.

The net costs of waste management, using incineration, will vary considerably depending upon the local conditions, the size and cost of the plant and the values of the heat and electricity sold. For larger plants, sited where energy can be sold locally, the net cost of incineration can be similar per tonne of waste treated to the costs of long distance landfill disposal. Electricity and heat sales help to offset some of the operating costs. (The environmental implications of burning refuse are discussed in Section 5.3.)

Foreign plants present a different approach: in Germany for example, the capital construction costs of such plants are shared by local authorities with a large proportion coming from central government (50 per cent). This financial support, with the introduction

---

32. Environmental Protection Act, 1990

Refuse

A number of methods are available for managing municipal waste products so as to ensure that the energy content of the wastes is not lost. The four principal options are: refuse incineration; decomposing refuse in landfill sites with recovery of gas; treating the waste in digesters; and the removal and recycling of certain types of waste.

Energy recovery is an important but not overiding consideration of waste management and should be balanced with other aspects of waste management: the need to reduce use of natural resources; the competing use of wood wastes and straw as compost material; and the need to lessen the risk to water sources from leaking landfill sites. Operating energy recovery schemes need not be incompatible with a national commitment to increase levels of material recovery through recycling. Studies by Warren Spring Laboratory, a national research centre, suggest that even when substantial quantities of paper, cardboard, plastics, textiles and other recyclables have been removed from the waste stream, two thirds of the energy content still remains.

of stringent regulations, has encouraged intensive development of high efficiency plants capable of meeting the standards imposed [33].

In smaller catchment areas, production of 'waste derived fuel' may be a more appropriate option. Waste derived fuel is produced from municipal solid waste and consists mainly of paper and plastic film. It is easier to handle and store than raw muncipal solid waste and presents less of a health risk. Waste derived fuel is currently being produced at half a dozen plants in the UK. A typical plant handling 85,000 tonnes of municipal solid waste per year might produce 20,000 tonnes of waste derived fuel, capable of generating around 6 MW of electricity. However, waste derived fuel is a comparatively low grade fuel with a low bulk density and is expensive to produce.

Top: Straw-Burning: One of Denmark's latest straw-fired district heating schemes is at Haslev, just south of Copenhagen. The plant burns 10 large bales an hour, 56,000 per year (around 28,000 tonnes of straw). It produces 13 MW of heat and 5 MW of electricity, which is exported to the grid. The heat is distributed to some 2,000 dwellings as well as schools and factories. The plant meets the entire system's heating load in the summer and about 70 per cent in the winter. It has a gas-fired back-up system. Straw is bought from local farmers who are paid tariffs related to the moisture content and delivery date. The dryer the straw and the later in the year the delivery, the higher the price.

Above: Kilns: At a sawmill in Caerphilly, operated by Western Softwood Ltd, almost 700 tonnes of green sawdust and woodchips from the company's operations are burnt each year in a fixed grate, underfed stoker furnace to kiln dry 3,000 cubic metres of timber. The system cost £105,000 to install and had a payback time of just over 4 years.

33. Energy Technology Support Unit, 1990a

Biological Processes

Landfill Gas

Decomposing refuse in landfill sites produces a gas with a calorific value half to two thirds that of natural gas. It can be recovered by sinking wells into the landfill and used for industrial heat or on-site electricity generation. If carbon dioxide is removed, the gas can also be injected directly into the gas grid. Theoretically, one tonne of refuse can yield 400 cubic metres of gas over a period of 10 years or so [34], though difficulties involved in capturing the gas may reduce the recoverable amount to between a quarter and a half of the theoretical potential. Tapping gas from landfill provides 2-4 times less recoverable energy per tonne than can be obtained by direct combustion of the waste - this includes energy from plastics which are not broken down in landfill.

Burning gas from existing sites rather than allowing it simply to seep out and escape would make a useful contribution to reducing greenhouse gas emissions and prevent accidental explosions involving methane build-up [35]. Although burning the methane gas itself produces carbon dioxide, this is a less potent greenhouse gas than methane.

By the beginning of 1990, there were over 240 landfill gas projects in operation worldwide, with about one third of these in the US - the largest, in New York, producing 150,000 cubic metres of gas per day. Germany had some 70 commercial schemes, the UK, 35, and there were a few schemes operating in France, Holland, and elsewhere in Europe. The UK schemes were saving an estimated 250,000 tonnes of coal per year, a figure which is expected to double by 1992 [36]. At some sites the gas is used to fire brick kilns, and at others, to "produce" steam in industry or generate electricity.

Waste Digesters

Treating wet wastes (including some types of refuse) in tanks, by anaerobic digestion, not only reduces odour and produces a less noxious effluent, but also generates combustible gas which can be used for direct heating or hot water production. Anaerobic digestion is being investigated as an alternative disposal option for municipal solid waste. The technology has been used for years in sewage treatment, and now treats about 60 per cent of sewage sludge in the UK where costs for a typical digester work out at about £15 per head of population. About one third of the gas produced is flared, but the rest is recovered to provide electricity and heat. Another application is for intensive livestock farming where housed livestock excrete some 7 million tonnes of faeces and urine each year with a gross energy content equivalent to 4 million tonnes of coal.

Energy Crops

Timber production from the UK's 2 million hectares of forests is about 4 million (dry) tonnes per year, with a gross energy content of 70 - 80 PJ. Looking beyond the turn of the century, output could be increased further by greater afforestation. One analysis suggests that there is potential for developing 150,000 sq kms of land specifically for forests, equivalent to 6.5 per cent of UK land area, and that this might produce 12-20 million tonnes of wood per year with a gross energy content equivalent to 9-15 million tonnes of coal [37].

Afforestation, particularly with conifers, is a fiercely controversial issue. There is, however, considerable potential for developing farm forests on 'surplus' arable land. These should not be confined to conifer monocultures but should encourage a diverse mix of species planted as single stem and coppiced woodland, with minimal inputs of pesticides and use of nitrogen-fixing species where possible, to reduce fertiliser requirements.

34. Richards, ETSU, 1987
35. Flood, 1989
36. Richards, 1989
37. Mitchel and Matthews, 1980

Top: Prefabricated Digesters: Farm Gas produces a range of prefabricated digesters for use in sewage treatment and other wastes. They are made from insulated Glass Reinforced Plastic. Small ones (of 20 cubic metres capacity) will handle the wastes created by a population of around 1,000 people; and large ones, up to 50,000. In total, more than 250 digesters are now in use in the UK.

Above: Landfill Gas: At Shanks and McEwen's Stewartby brick works, 50 miles north of London, landfill gas has been used for more than a decade to fire kilns. It is also used to generate electricity using three 275 kW gas engines. Surplus power is sold to the local electricity distribution company.

Right: Short rotation forestry trials

A Programme for the UK

Though interest in energy-from-waste projects in the UK has grown in recent years in view of the serious environmental problems caused by landfilling, development has been piecemeal. This experience contrasts with that in Scandinavia, where governments have taken steps to ensure that indigenous biofuel residues are put to use rather than being wasted. Sweden produced 220 PJ of energy from indigenous biofuels during 1989 (15 per cent of primary energy), including almost one third of its district heating. Potential for a further 50 TWh of power has been identified by the Swedish state electricity company and the Government is spending £90 million over the next five years developing biomass. Denmark has established over 30 straw-fired and 23 wood-chip fired district heating plants in the last 10 years. It has, in addition, about 40 municipal waste incinerators providing heat for district heating networks [38].

The UK has three and a half times the combined populations of Sweden and Denmark, and much greater national resources. There are many major conurbations without adequate landfill capacity and with high heat loads suitable for district heating. In theory, a national programme of energy-from-biofuels could involve introducing measures to encourage:

■ harnessing the full potential of methane generated in existing landfill sites (about 200 MW by the year 2000, generating electricity equivalent to a primary energy value of 15.6 per year).

■ straw burning in rural areas, with targets of perhaps 2 million tonnes per year by 2005 (30 PJ) and 4 million tonnes per year by 2020 (60 PJ). This represents using about one third and two thirds of annual straw production respectively.

■ the use of wood residues as fuel, with targets of perhaps 0.5 million tonnes per year by 2005 (7.5 PJ) and 2 million tonnes per year by 2020 (30 PJ).

■ a programme to integrate recycling and energy recovery needs to involve the replacement of current combustion plants with new plant for electricity and district heating for the main conurbations over the next 15-20 years, handling 10-12 million tonnes per year of municipal solid wastes (equivalent to 70-100 PJ).

■ the digestion of wet wastes, especially on intensive livestock farms and in the food industry, with targets of perhaps 1.8 million tonnes (dry wt) per year (18 PJ) by 2005 and 3.5 million tonnes per year (35 PJ) by 2020.

■ the planting of trees for fuel with a target of 2 million tonnes per year (30 PJ) in the short term and 15 million tonnes per year (225 PJ) in the longer term.

Taken together these measures could produce 160 PJ per year of primary energy by 2005, and 480 PJ by 2020 (5.5 per cent of current primary energy use).

38. Danish Ministry of Energy, 1990

Biofuels Summary Box:

1. Possible future contribution from renewable energy, identifying contribution from biofuels

**a) Primary Energy Equivalent
(combining heat and electricity)**

b) Electricity

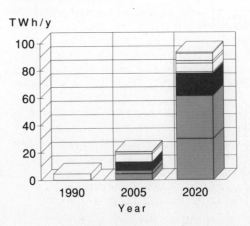

2. UK Research and Development Budget (in 1990-91 prices) [Source: Hansard, 10 July 1989]

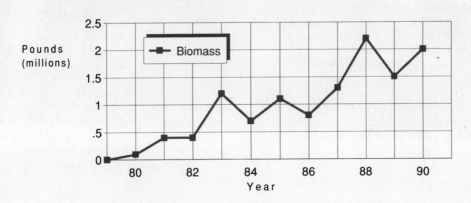

3.3 Solar Energy

Despite its northern latitude, the UK receives roughly half as much solar energy as some of the sunniest parts of the world. In theory, there is sufficient solar energy in the UK to provide all of the space and water heating of well-designed dwellings. In practice, seasonal swings in availability make year-round solar heating impractical. The fact that about half of the incoming solar energy in the UK is in the form of scattered, diffuse light which cannot be focused using mirrors and lenses rules out building thermal solar power stations like those now working successfully in California, but there are other things we can do.

Solar Architecture

Buildings with large south-facing and small north-facing windows and high levels of thermal insulation, can trap the Sun's energy and store it as heat within the structure. This 'free heat' is then distributed around the building by the processes of conduction, convection and thermal radiation, keeping the inside comfortable when the outside temperature falls. Increased use of daylight also reduces the need for artificial lighting which is of major importance in commercial buildings. It also reduces the commercial air-conditioning load, because less heat is released into buildings from electrical lighting systems.

Over the past decade, hundreds of thousands of buildings incorporating these so-called 'passive solar' features have been erected - even in Alaska. Integrating passive solar design with energy efficiency measures can reduce energy consumption in new housing for both heating and lighting. Heating bills can be cut by more than half for little extra cost. For existing buildings, passive solar features, including conservatories and glazed courtyards can be fitted during major rehabilitation work.

There are many examples of solar buildings in the UK. The highest concentration is in Milton Keynes, where there are over 200 solar dwellings. Unfortunately, it is often difficult to make best use of solar gains in existing towns and cities because road layouts and land values impose constraints on the way buildings are orientated. Nevertheless, the

Department of Energy has estimated the potential for passive solar as equivalent to 2-4 per cent of current energy use for the UK.

A study of space heating in buildings, carried out by the Building Research Establishment, estimated that some 15 per cent of domestic space heating in the UK comes from the incidental solar heat in buildings. This substantial energy supply means that solar already provides as much heat as coal, oil and electricity combined for the domestic sector (see Figure 3.7).

Figure 3.7: How the home is heated [39]

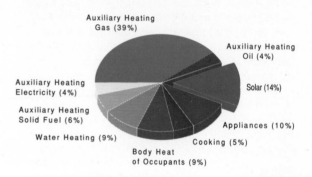

Active Solar Heating

At the moment, costs are prohibitively high for solar water heating, although there is considerable potential for cost reduction through design improvement and mass production of advanced systems. Enhanced performance systems do already exist: in the vacuum tube collector, for example, a blackened absorber is sealed inside an evacuated glass tube to eliminate conduction and convection losses; selective surfaces and heat mirrors can minimise radiant heat losses; a simple non-focusing system can generate temperatures as high as 200°C and can respond very rapidly to changes in the intensity of the light, converting sunlight into useful heat even when outside temperatures are well below freezing.

39. Doggart & Flood, 1989

In future, it may become worthwhile to provide year-round solar heating for small groups of dwellings by coupling up banks of solar collectors to a sunken interseasonal heat store (see Section 4.5). Solar energy could also make an input into large district heating schemes [40]. For individual dwellings, active solar space heating with a payback period of about 20 years is not economic using current cost assumptions.

Solar Cells (photovoltaics)

Solar cells are clean, safe and silent in operation, having no moving parts. They can be manufactured from silicon, the second most abundant element in the Earth's crust. Although at the moment they are an expensive method of generating electricity for the grid (between 3 and 6 times more expensive), they compete very successfully with conventional systems for a wide range of applications in remote locations. For example, solar cells provide power for refrigeration and water pumping in hot desert regions, and for telecommunication equipment on mountain tops.

The price of photovoltaic solar cells has fallen dramatically in recent years, and should fall further with the introduction of thin film systems to replace the previously-used single and polycrystalline cells. Some photovoltaics experts estimate that, by the turn of the century, solar cells will be cheap enough to be used as a replacement for conventional fossil fuel systems for grid supply in sunny locations. However, there are limits to how far prices will fall: 50 per cent of the cost of a photovoltaic system is accounted for by the support structure, mountings, interconnection and power conditioning, although even here, some costs can be offset if solar cells are built into existing structures, such as the roofs and walls of buildings.

The Department of Energy has estimated that, in principle, large scale photovoltaic power plants could supply more electricity than the total current UK requirement. To generate so much power would require some 6,000 square kilometres of arrays covering 2.5 per cent of the UK's land area. A recent Government report has suggested that photovoltaics could be a cost-effective power source for the UK in the next century, if they are installed as a wall or roof cladding on new buildings [41]. The area required to

Above: Passive Solar: Looe Junior and Infants School, Cornwall, was built in 1984. An estimated 40 per cent of the heating requirements of the school are met from direct solar gains. The south facade of the school is completely glazed. The cruciform shape of the structure allows all classrooms to face south with corridors and utility rooms positioned along the north facade. Floor, wall and roof insulation, double glazed windows and draught lobbies minimise heat loss. Despite the high level of finish and fabric specification, construction costs were only marginally above the average for primary school buildings.

Below: A block of two 2-bedroomed and two 3-bedroomed homes in Milton Keynes. South-facing living areas and conservatory, high levels of insulation to roof, walls and floor, draught-stripping and thermal heating store all ensure that savings of around 50 per cent per year are achieved compared to equivalent sized home built to standard building requirements.

40. IEA, 1990
41. Energy Technology Support Unit, 1991

Above: An 'atrium' (glass-covered area), at the JEL factory, Stockport.

Below: Solar cells at Work: This experimental house with a photovoltaic roof in Saarbrucken, Germany, was built in 1984. The roof panels, made from around 100 sq metres of polycrystalline silicon, belong to the owner, who sells surplus electricity to the local electricity board. The unit cost £60,000 to install, but it could be the forerunner of systems operating next century.

accommodate large amounts of photovoltaics (measured in thousands of megawatts) would be available without additional land-use. However, even when the cost of photovoltaics has fallen to the required level, there will still be problems in coping with the large seasonal variations in power (see Section 4.3).

A Solar Programme for The UK

Solar energy could play a much greater part in daily life in the UK, but more effort must first go into promoting passive solar design in buildings, and more money should be spent on research to bring down the cost of solar water heating and photovoltaics.

It is possible to increase substantially the contribution of solar energy in buildings by encouraging modifications to building design. With careful monitoring, and government action where necessary, at least 3 million passive solar buildings (new and retrofit) could be in place by 2020.

Further, the Government should reactivate its research programme on solar water heating which it virtually terminated in 1984 and support work aimed at reducing system costs. Similarly, research into solar group heating and interseasonal heat storage is now necessary.

The Department of Energy has never funded research into photovoltaics because it has not considered solar cells to have any significant potential for power production in the UK. The Department is now (1991) looking into funding research into the use of photovoltaics as a wall or roof cladding in buildings. The majority of funding for photovoltaics in the UK over the past 10 years has come from the European Community and this budget is also set to increase. However, adding together funding from all sources, the UK effort has been tiny compared to that of the USA (£21 million per year), Japan (£16 million per year) or Germany (£30 million per year). There is an urgent need to increase funds for both research and demonstration to ensure that the UK is able to compete in this rapidly growing field.

Solar Summary Box:

1. Possible future contribution from renewable energy, identifying contribution from solar

a) Primary Energy Equivalent
(combining heat and electricity)

b) Electricity

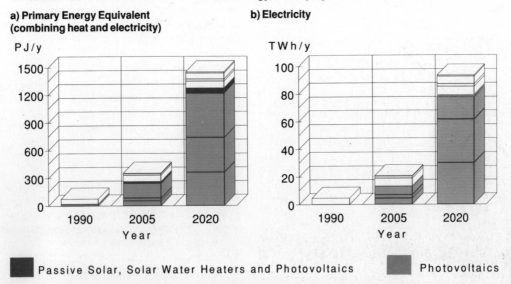

■ Passive Solar, Solar Water Heaters and Photovoltaics   ■ Photovoltaics

2. UK Budget for All Solar Research and Development (in 1990-91 prices) [Source: Hansard, 10 July 1989]

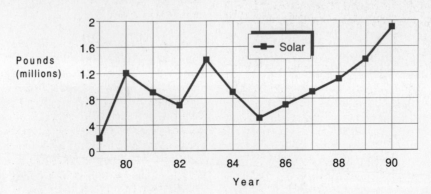

3.4 Water Power

Hydro-electricity

Water power has been used in the UK for centuries. Today about 50 large hydro-electric schemes (above 10 MW), and more than 20 smaller ones, are producing about 2 per cent of the country's electricity. Most schemes rely on dams to impound water in reservoirs. Others are 'run-of-river' and thus have no storage capacity, but rely on the diversion of water from a river through turbines. Output depends on the flow in the river. Existing schemes provide some of the cheapest electricity generated in the UK (around 0.75 pence per kWh), as the capital investment is now paid off. New schemes would be more expensive.

Several studies of the UK potential for hydro have been carried out [42]. One study put the technical potential for Scotland, for schemes above 50 kW in output, at 8.5 TWh per year (2,700 MW), over twice the currently installed capacity [43]. A study by Salford Civil Engineering Ltd put the economic potential for small hydro (down to 25 kW in output), at around 1.3 TWh per year (320 MW), with almost 90 per cent of this capacity in Scotland. There is considerable potential for plant below 25 kW, but a thorough study of the potential for so-called 'micro' hydro has not been done.

For large hydroelectric schemes (greater than 5 MW), many of the best sites have already been developed, but the contribution from hydroelectricity could be increased by building a large number of small schemes and redeveloping existing dams. It may ultimately be possible to treble the contribution from hydroelectric power (which would amount to about 5 per cent of current electricity use).

A Programme for the UK

The UK potential for small and micro hydro should be assessed and a programme developed to build on the results of this study, giving particular emphasis on making fuller use of the hydroelectric resource in Scotland.

42. See Jackson, 1988, for a review.
43. The study was conducted by the then North of Scotland Hydro Electric Board.

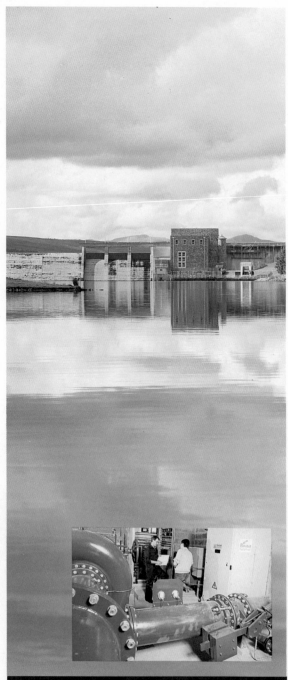

Main picture: Lairg hydro-electric power station, Scotland. Inset: Turbines for small hydro-electric plant, Scotland.

Hydro-electricity Summary Box:

1. Possible future contribution from renewable energy, identifying contribution from hydro-electricity

a) As Primary Energy Equivalent　　　　**b) As Electricity**

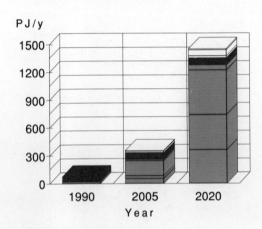

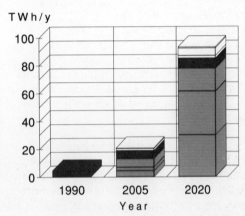

2. Generation Cost [Source: Laughton, 1990]

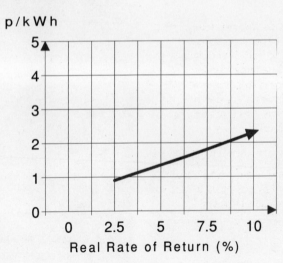

Tidal Energy

Less than a century ago, over 100 small tide mills were in operation around the UK's coast. Though these mills are now gone, the potential in the tides remains.

Tidal barrages can be built across bays or estuaries where there is a high tidal range (more than about 4 metres). The technology is well understood (see cross-sectional diagram, Figure 3.8, right): several schemes are operating abroad, including the 240 MW scheme at La Rance in Britanny and a 20 MW scheme in Canada.

Figure 3.8: Cross sectional diagram of a tidal barrage showing bulb turbine

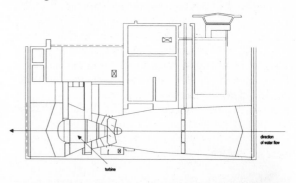

La Rance: The Tidal Power Station at La Rance in Britanny is the most famous, and easily the biggest, tidal power station in the world. It has 24 large reversible bulb turbines housed in a barrage 750 metres long. It operates on both the ebb and flood tides, and can generate 240 megawatts of electricity. The output from the scheme is around 500 million kilowatt hours per year.

The technical potential for estuarine tidal power in the UK has been estimated at around 54 TWh per year [44], one sixth of current electricity demand. It could be much higher if practical ways can be found to build tidal barrages in shallow coastal waters outside of estuaries. Nine tenths of the potential is at eight sites including the Mersey, the Severn, the Solway Firth, Morecambe Bay, and the Wash. The remainder comes from 34 small sites, with each yielding typically 20-100 GWh per year [45]. A barrage across the estuary at Padstow in Cornwall, for example, might provide up to 30 MW of power and generate around 55 GWh of electricity per year.

Pre-feasibility studies have been completed for tidal energy barrages on the Loughor and Conwy Estuaries in Wales and more detailed studies of two other possible tidal schemes, for the Mersey and Severn Estuaries, are at an advanced stage. For the Mersey site, the proposed barrage would be 1.75 kilometres long; it would have 28 turbines and would generate 1.5 TWh per year (700 MW peak). A barrage across the Severn would stretch approximately 17 kilometres. It would have an installed capacity of 8.64 GW [46] and might supply 15 TWh of electricity per year (almost 6 per cent of current UK use). Estimates put the cost of such a scheme at more than £9 billion.

Operating large schemes would present few difficulties in the UK because of the size of the electricity grid which can easily absorb predictable fluctuations in output. (The environmental implications of tidal barrages are discussed in Section 5.3).

A Programme for the UK

Whether or not individual tidal schemes should go ahead depends as much on considerations of wildlife and regional development as on the value of the energy produced and the pollution avoided. At the present time, expenditure to support the construction of large tidal power plants cannot be justified when balancing the costs and impacts of such barrages with their energy benefits. Nevertheless, circumstances change. Proposals for large tidal barrages should therefore be kept under review and re-examined periodically in the light of wider national and international considerations, not least global warming. In addition, the Government should continue to support generic research into the environmental impacts of large tidal barrages, in order to clarify the major uncertainties in this area.

Notwithstanding possible large tidal barrage developments, there is a need for the Government to increase its commitment to small scale tidal energy work. Currently only about £100,000 per year, or 5 per cent of Department of Energy funding on tidal research is devoted to small scale development. This work should focus on supporting construction of one or more small scale demonstration barrages to establish the technology for the UK.

44. Department of Energy, 1988a
45. Binnie, 1987
46. This is equivalent to 2.9 GW of conventional plant, after allowing for the variations in output through intermittency.

Tidal Summary Box:

1. Possible future contribution from renewable energy, identifying contribution from tidal power

a) As Primary Energy Equivalent

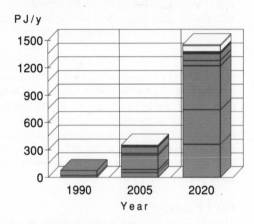

b) As Electricity

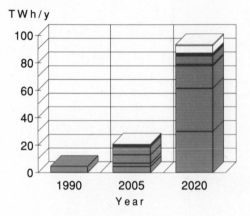

2. Generation Cost [Source: Laughton, 1990]

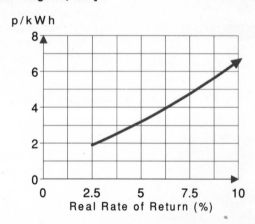

3. UK Research and Development Budget (in 1990-91 prices) [Source: Hansard, 10 July 1989]

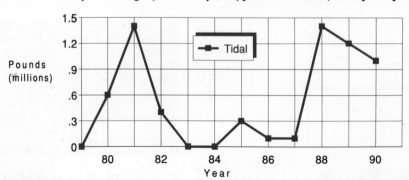

Wave Power

People have speculated on using wave power for centuries - the first patent for a wave energy converter was taken out in 1799. Despite this, and the obvious potential, wave energy is amongst the least developed of the renewable energy technologies.

Many different wave energy devices have been proposed and a number of prototypes have been built. Some are shore-mounted, others are designed for operation in the more hostile deep sea environment where the energy content in the waves may average as much as 50 kW per metre of wave front (equivalent to 50 single bar electric fires for each metre).

The UK Resource

The UK is well-placed to tap the large energy resource of ocean waves. The energy available from waves matches the pattern of electricity demand in the UK, since in winter both the power in the waves and the demand for electricity are greatest. If the technical challenge can be met, even the more pessimistic estimates [47] suggest that wave energy could supply up to one-sixth of current UK electricity - some studies put the potential at well over one third.

Left: Oscillating Water Column: This prototype wave energy station near Bergen in Norway was destroyed in a storm. The device consisted of a 20 metre high cylinder open at the base. Waves striking the device caused oscillations in a column of water trapped inside the chamber. The water acted like a piston forcing air through an overhead turbine, driving a 500 kW generator. The device has been substantially redesigned in concrete with a horizontal mounting and reconstruction is planned.

47. Energy Technology Support Unit, 1985a

The Demise of the UK's Wave Power Programme

The UK's wave energy research programme, which led the world in the 1970s, was dismantled in 1982 when the Government decided that none of the devices then being investigated were likely to produce competitively-priced electricity for grid supply [48]. However, the programme was badly mishandled and there were a number of serious short-comings: poor project management; over-cumbersome reviews; shortage of money for testing and trials; unrealistic design specifications and pessimistic cost and reliability assumptions. New costing techniques were also developed which unfairly penalised wave energy conversion systems because of weight.

One report which originally showed that the cost of electricity from the Salter Duck would be 9.8 pence per kWh was withdrawn after a bitter fight; the revised assessment was 5.2 pence per kWh at 1986 rates [49]. The wave energy research programme itself was directed towards designing a massive 2,000 MW 'Reference Design' wave energy station notionally sited off the West Coast of Scotland - a task that can be likened to designing a supertanker whilst at the same time developing the principles of naval architecture.

The Circular Clam: The Clam, developed by Coventry Polytechnic, has rows of air bags which are squeezed by passing waves forcing air through turbines mounted on a floating quoit-shaped structure. A 60 metre diameter device with one dozen segments would have an average output of around 600 kW (2 MW installed).

48. Energy Technology Support Unit, 1985a
49. Salter, 1988; 1990

However, virtually all research has ceased due to a government freeze on funding. Despite this, there is still interest in a number of devices, for example, the Salter Duck (Edinburgh University), the SEA Clam (Coventry Polytechnic), the Oscillating Water Column (Belfast University, National Engineering Laboratory), and inertia devices like the Frog (Lancaster University) [50]. Very little government money is going into wave energy, though a small (180 kW) shoreline device has been built and is now undergoing tests on the Isle of Islay in Scotland. A survey of possible coastal sites is also underway, the results of which are expected to be announced at the end of 1991.

Work Overseas
Though very little work is currently being conducted overseas on off-shore wave energy devices, much work is being undertaken for on-shore devices. The Norwegians were the first to build prototype wave energy converters of any size: two were completed around 1985 on a site just north of Bergen [51]. The Japanese have also put major resources into wave energy and are currently investigating about ten shoreline or nearshore devices [52]. Portugal, Denmark, Sweden and India have also undertaken some research into wave energy.

One Norwegian device called 'Tapchan', is built into a natural inlet in the cliff and has a rated output of 350 kW. A tapering concrete channel 170 metres long with vertical walls funnels breakers over a low dam. The overspill is impounded in an artificial reservoir 3 metres above sea level and discharged back to sea via a conventional low head turbine. The Norwegians are trying to build an overseas market for this device and the oscillating water column, targetting mostly island countries in the Pacific Ocean where they believe there could be a substantial market and where the costs are competitive with conventional electricity sources, primarily diesel.

A Programme for the UK
Realising wave energy's potential requires a major long-term commitment, with money being put into re-establishing a number of wave energy research teams. The ultimate objective should be the completion of commercial off-shore wave devices, where the greatest potential for the UK exists. The first step should be to establish an integrated wave energy research programme to prove the technology both on-shore and in shallow waters. Afterwards, work should concentrate on proving the technology fully off-shore. Targets for exploiting the country's wave energy resources should then be established. This programme should involve:

■ Fundamental and generic research (costing £10 million spread over 12 years);

■ Further work on actual devices, including the construction of a second shore-line demonstration unit, component testing and research for a full-scale off-shore pilot project (costing possibly £5 million spread over three years); and

■ Building a full-scale off-shore device, should the research findings warrant this (which might require £12 million spread over 3 years).

In addition, there should be a broader programme to refine device concepts and improve performance and cost-effectiveness (£1 million per year). The successful completion of such a programme might see the first commercial wave energy stations in operation by around the turn of the century [53].

50. These devices are described in eg: Energy Technology Support Unit, 1985a; Lewis, 1985; and Evans, 1988.
51. Steen, 1985
52. Department of Energy Progress Report, 1990
53. Duckers, 1990

Wave Summary Box:

1. Possible future contribution from renewable energy, identifying contribution from wave power

a) As Primary Energy Equivalent

b) As Electricity

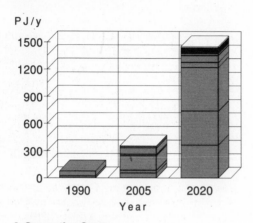

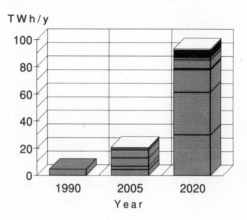

**2. Generation Costs
[Source: Laughton, 1990]**

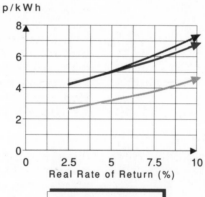

3. UK Research and Development Budget (in 1990-91 prices) [Source: Hansard, 10 July 1989]

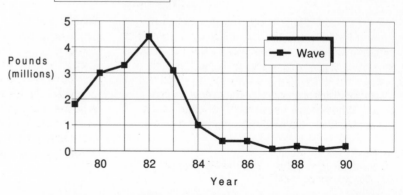

3.5 Geothermal Energy

Within the top 10 kilometres of the Earth's crust - at depths accessible with current drilling techniques - there is sufficient heat to meet all of the UK's energy needs for hundreds and perhaps even thousands of years. The challenge lies in finding ways to harness this heat.

The heat flows out from the Earth's molten interior, and is enhanced in some rocks by heat from natural radioactive decay. Temperature gradients beneath the UK lie in the range 20-40°C per vertical kilometre, with the highest rates recorded in the dry granite rock of the South West of England. Here, the temperature 3 kilometres down is high enough to boil water, and at 6 kilometres, to produce steam at more than 200°C (sufficient to generate electricity). Whether the UK can tap into its vast geothermal resources will depend on the development of Hot Dry Rock (HDR) technology.

Hot Dry Rock Geothermal

Hot dry rock geothermal involves pumping water through rock which has been artificially fractured at depths of several kilometres, and then recovering superheated water or steam (see Figure 3.9 over). Strictly speaking, hot dry rock geothermal is a 'non-renewable' resource - the heat from a reservoir is available for extraction only once as it takes thousands of years for the temperature of the granite to return. It does, however, offer a relatively clean alternative to conventional fuels.

The British Geological Survey, which carried out an assessment of the accessible geothermal hot dry rock resource, has pointed out that if it were possible to recover just 1 per cent of the energy beneath the country using hot dry rock techniques this could amount to 100,000 TWh, about 400 times current UK electricity use [54]. The resource in Cornwall is large enough to supply all the electricity requirements of the south-western, southern and south-eastern electricity distribution companies over a 25 year period. Whether this happens or not depends on being able to develop the resource economically.

54. Downing *et al*, 1986
55. Sunderland Polytechnic / Sheffield City Polytechnic, 1990;
RTZ Consultants Ltd, 1991

The technology of hot dry rock geothermal is still at the experimental stage, with many difficult problems still to be overcome. While the principle of hot dry rock has been proven, its suitability for the UK is not yet certain.

Technical Challenge
Technical developments still need to be made: learning how to drill through hard and abrasive rocks in very hot and chemically corrosive environments; learning how to achieve reservoirs of fractured rock of the correct size and shape, and establish satisfactory flow rates; learning how to reduce water loss from the reservoir to acceptable levels; and understanding the properties of rocks at the 6 kilometres depths needed for commercial hot dry rock reservoirs.

A team of scientists at the Camborne School of Mines in Cornwall has already made considerable progress in developing systems for harnessing the technology. In 1982 the team created a large reservoir of fractured rock two to three kilometres below ground in granite, and was able to extract heat by circulating water under pressure through cracks and fissures in the rock. The temperature of the water was found to drop from 80°C to 55°C due to a 'short-circuit' of the water reservoir. Experiments are now planned to seal off the short-circuit permanently and thereby prevent the continuing temperature fall.

Two reviews completed recently have indicated that although it is difficult to determine the economics of hot dry rock accurately because of the technical uncertainties, electricity from a commercial-size hot dry rock power station could cost between two and ten times more than electricity generated by conventional means [55].

Work Overseas
The United States, Germany, Japan, France and Sweden are also involved in hot dry rock drilling, fracture stimulation and circulation experiments. None of this work is as advanced as that in the UK. A proposed European geothermal research programme includes a possible experimental prototype, after first carrying out feasibility studies on sites in France, Germany and the UK with the intention of selecting a suitable site by about 1992.

Geothermal Group Heating

Lower temperature heat (60-75°C), suitable for space and water heating, can be recovered from much shallower depths at less cost using conventional techniques; for example, drilling into natural aquifers 2-3 kilometres down and pumping up water. This is now being done on an increasing scale, for example in Hungary, the Soviet Union and France. (France has actually commissioned more than 60 schemes in the last 20 years, mainly in Paris and Bordeaux.) The water may be salty and highly corrosive and heat must therefore be extracted with a heat exchanger or heat pump. The heat can then be distributed from the wellhead to neighbouring district heating schemes, or to industry. A single well will supply, typically, around 5 MW of heat, enough for perhaps 70 per cent of the space and water-heating needs for 2,000 dwellings. (The largest schemes supply heat to nearly 10,000 dwellings.)

Drilling for hot water involves significant financial risks, which in France have been under-written by the Government. Three out of four trial wells in the UK have been abandoned because flow rates have been too low to make group heating schemes economic. Nevertheless, more schemes might be attempted, for example in the Bournemouth and Poole area, around Grimsby, and possibly Crewe where the prospects look brightest. Good groundwater conditions can be found over about half of the area of England and in localised parts of Scotland and Wales.

Heat pumps can be used to increase the temperature of water from shallow aquifers or ground water: they are widely used in some parts of the United States for heating farm buildings, hospitals, schools and even single dwellings. In the last few years similar schemes have been undertaken in Western Europe. One large scheme at Lund in Sweden supplies heat to 2,500 single family houses with the aid of a 20 MW heat pump. Water (at only 23°C) is drawn from an aquifer 700 meters below ground and is then pumped 5 kilometres to the estate.

Below: Southampton: There is one geothermal heating scheme in the UK, which serves shops and offices in Southampton. It draws hot water (at around 75°C) from an aquifer under the city. The annual heat production is estimated to be 26 TJ. The scheme is expected to have a lifespan of 20 years.

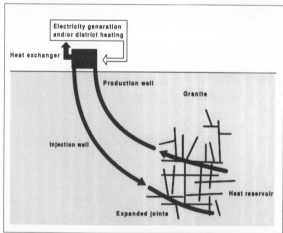

Figure 3.9: Hot Dry Rock: The technique for extracting heat from hot dry rock was originally developed in the US and involves drilling two wells to depths of 6 or 7 kilometres. This could take up to a year. The wells are one above the other and are 'bent' in the shape of the letter 'J'. Joints or fissures in the rock are opened up by forcing water down one of the wells at very high pressures (around 300 atmospheres), with small explosive charges used to break up the rock around the base of the wells.

Geothermal Summary Box:

1. Possible future contribution from renewable energy, identifying contribution from geothermal

a) Primary Energy Equivalent
(combining heat and electricity)

b) Electricity

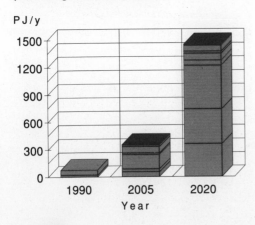

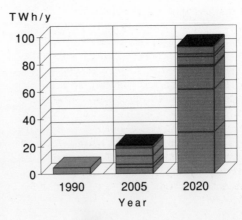

| Hot Aquiver and Hot Dry Rock | Hot Dry Rock |

2. Generation Costs (HDR)
[Source: Sunderland
Polytechnic, 1990]

p / k W h

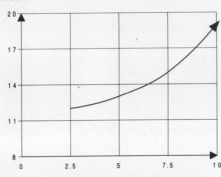

3. UK Research and
Development Budget (in
1990-91 prices) [Source:
Hansard, 10 July 1989]

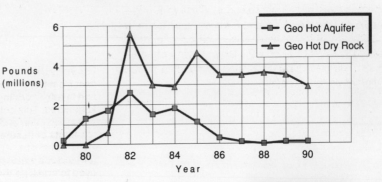

A Programme for the UK

The Government announced in early 1991 that it was concentrating hot dry rock support on the European programme. It is assisting this research by contributing £3.3 million over a three year period. However, the application of hot dry rock is highly site-specific - technical reseach experience gained at one site is of limited value for another site. It is therefore important that the UK does not spend money on developing hot dry rock technology in the Euopean context without also continuing to support projects in the UK itself.

For the UK, a future work programme should address the fundamental problems which constrain the technology. This might include further drilling to a target depth of 6 kilometres, the depth at which exploitation of the technology would ultimately take place.

Figure 3.10: Possible future contributions from all renewable energy by 2005 and 2020 *

a) Primary Energy Equivalent (combining heat and electricity)

b) Electricity

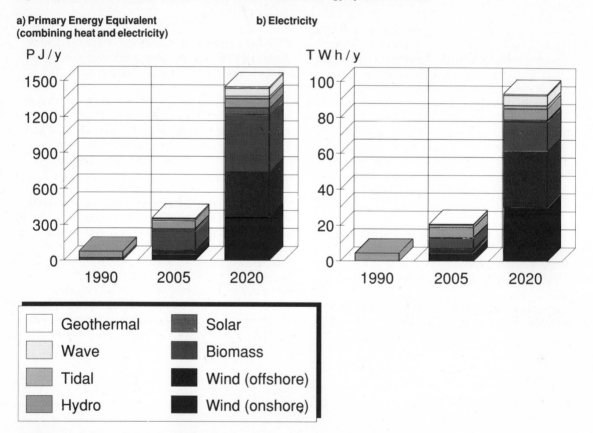

* (excluding current contribution from solar, estimated to be about 15 per cent of heating for buildings, see page 35)

4. A New Energy Path for the UK

"It should be possible over a few decades to redesign and rebuild the entire structure to supply the services for which energy is needed - heat, light, cold, motive power, and so forth - at a fraction of the costs, primary energy consumption and pollution outputs which we now suffer. It is 'only' ignorance, lack of political will, the present dominance of energy supply over demand-side thinking, and of 'react and cure' over 'anticipate and prevent' politics, which stand in the way of such a potentially beneficial upheaval."

Gerald Leach & Zygfryd Nowak, 1990 [56]

To achieve sustainable, environmentally sound development, the UK will need to adopt a radically different energy policy from the one it has been pursuing since the Second World War. The essence of such a policy is to meet the nation's demand for *energy services* as efficiently and cleanly as possible.

That is not the same as meeting demand for *energy* - an excuse used continually over the last forty years by politicians seeking to justify building a new power station, opening a new oil pipe-line or drilling a new gas field. People do not want electricity, oil or gas; they want the *services* which can be provided by using such fuels in hardware like buildings, boilers, appliances, motors, and light bulbs, for warmth, cooked and cooled food, mobility, light and so on. The demand to be met is for these energy services. The challenge of the new energy path is to meet that demand whilst minimising the impact on the environment.

This means that the renewable energy technologies described in the previous chapter must play an increasingly important role. This chapter gives a brief overview of the other vital components of this path:

■ a determined drive to stamp out the inefficient use of energy in all sectors of the economy (Section 4.1);

■ the introduction of cleaner and more efficient fossil fuel burning technologies (Section 4.2);

■ the widespread adoption of combined heat and power, making use of the 'waste' heat from electricity generation for heating and industrial processes (Section 4.2); and

■ the development of techniques for storing energy to make greater use of those sources of renewable energy which are intermittent (Section 4.4).

Renewable energy and energy efficiency go hand-in-hand; there is clearly very little point in going to all the trouble and expense to recover renewable energy with low impact technologies unless it is used sensibly in energy efficient buildings, vehicles and appliances.

Of course, whatever measures are taken to reduce our dependence on coal, oil, natural gas and uranium and however fast renewable energy technologies are introduced, there will remain a need to use fossil fuels for the foreseeable future. The emphasis must therefore be on cleaner and more efficient technologies for burning fossil fuels. In addition, research into efficient energy storage systems is a priority to maximise the benefits and potential of the intermittent renewables like the sun and the wind.

---

56. Stockholm Environment Institute, 1990

4.1 Energy Efficiency and Pollution Reduction

Over the last decade, numerous research reports have highlighted the substantial cost-effective technical potential for reducing UK primary energy demand through improvements in energy efficiency (see Box 4.1). Technologies are now available to reduce the amount of fossil fuels and electricity needed to provide the energy services we increasingly take for granted. These range from compact fluorescent light bulbs which use 80 per cent less electricity than standard bulbs for the same light output, to buildings designed to minimise heat loss and maximise use of the sun's warmth and light.

Box 4.1: From Energy Saving to Carbon Cutting

Detailed studies of the potential for energy efficiency improvements in the UK date back to 1979 when Gerald Leach showed that even with a trebling of UK economic output, primary energy demand could be cut by one fifth by the year 2020 using then-existing technology. A more detailed study four years later [57] broke down potential savings by each end use and concluded that a 55 - 60 per cent cut in primary energy use was possible by 2025, despite a continually rising standard of living.

Both studies tempered the actual technical potential for energy efficiency with political realities, assuming that technologies in use would not be scrapped before the end of their useful life and that only those efficiency measures which were economically viable would be undertaken.

More recently, studies have turned to assessing the reductions in pollution available from improving energy efficiency and switching to less polluting energy sources. A report for Friends of the Earth, for example, used mainly Government-sponsored studies to demonstrate that the economic potential exists to cut carbon dioxide emissions from the non-transport energy sector by roughly 50 per cent from current levels by 2005 [58].

Another study in 1990 [59] showed that even with "quite modest" assumptions about the introduction of efficiency improvements, the UK could cut carbon dioxide emissions from current levels by 20 - 25 per cent by 2005 whilst knocking a massive £119 billion in total off energy bills between 1987 and 2005. During this period the authors allowed for economic growth in line with trends from 1950 - 1988.

Technically, two-thirds or more of UK primary energy could be saved if these energy efficient buildings, appliances, vehicles and electricity generating techniques became the norm rather than the exception (see Box 4.2). The technologies themselves and their applications are simple, well tried and well tested. Moreover, improvements in

Box 4.2: Energy Efficient Technologies - Some Examples

Heating buildings
Heating existing buildings accounts for 30 per cent of UK energy use. By reducing ventilation rates with draughtproofing, insulating walls, roofs, floors and windows, and improving electronic controls of heating systems, the energy needed to keep a building warm in winter could be cut in half. For new buildings, design and construction techniques exist which can virtually do away with the need for space heating. Even using conventional techniques, by increasing insulation levels and improving boiler efficiencies, energy use can be more than halved when compared with standard 'new build' housing and offices. For future design, specially coated glass for windows is now becoming available which cuts heat loss from the building by seven-fold compared even with ordinary double glazing.

Getting Around
Transportation accounts for around 32 per cent of UK energy use. There is a need to turn to high efficiency cars which make use of lighter materials, electronic tuning systems, direct fuel injection and more stream-lined bodywork. Some major car manufacturers have pre-production prototypes which can travel more than 100 miles per gallon with little loss of associated engine performance. In addition, mass transport like buses and trains are far more energy efficient than cars, in terms of getting passengers or freight over a certain distance. Developing these services and land-use planning policies to reduce transport demand are vital to a new energy path in the UK.

Cooling Food
The most energy efficient mass-produced fridges and freezers use 70 - 75 per cent less electricity than average appliances on sale in the UK today. A typical fridge on sale uses around 270 units of electricity (kilowatt-hours) a year, whereas the best models available in Europe use just 80 units a year to cool their contents. Laboratory prototypes, using highly insulating vacuum-sealed panels, can do the same job for just 40 units a year [60].

57. Olivier *et al*, 1983
58. Jackson and Roberts, 1989
59. Leach and Nowak, 1990

60. Friends of the Earth Evidence to House of Lords European Communities Committee, Feb 1989; Energy Efficiency Office, 1990; Norgard, 1989

energy efficiency make economic sense, particularly as a cheaper alternative to investing in new power stations, oil refineries or mining equipment. Improving energy efficiency can mean meeting the UK demand for energy services using less fossil fuel and electricity, leading to a far lower impact on the environment, while spending a smaller proportion of the nation's economic resources doing so.

However, while energy efficiency makes sense, the technical and economic potential for improvements is not being realised. Many obstacles and barriers to the introduction of energy efficiency measures exist because of the economic, institutional and social background to energy policy in the UK. These have been documented in some detail elsewhere [61] and range from householders lacking the finances to insulate their cavity walls to the complexities of the structure and regulation of the electricity and gas industries.

It need not be like this. For example, regulations can be developed to ensure that electricity companies can make greater profits from improving the energy efficiency of their consumers' lighting systems than from selling the electricity to power inefficient systems.

The ability of the UK or any other country to improve its energy efficiency is not constrained by technical limitations but by political ones. The challenge to the Government is therefore to introduce policies which redirect the specific interests and profit motives of many different sectors in the energy market, so as to ensure that investments in energy efficiency improvements are undertaken to maximise the efficient use of the nation's economic resources and minimise impact on the environment.

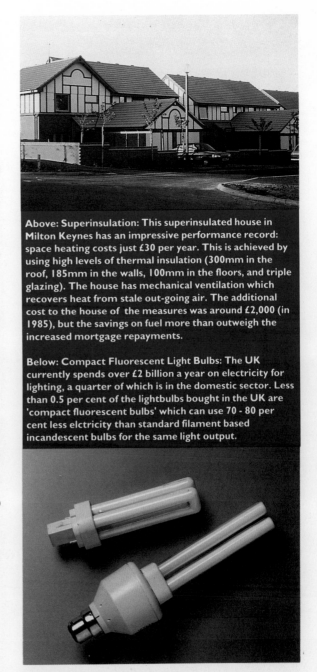

Above: Superinsulation: This superinsulated house in Milton Keynes has an impressive performance record: space heating costs just £30 per year. This is achieved by using high levels of thermal insulation (300mm in the roof, 185mm in the walls, 100mm in the floors, and triple glazing). The house has mechanical ventilation which recovers heat from stale out-going air. The additional cost to the house of the measures was around £2,000 (in 1985), but the savings on fuel more than outweigh the increased mortgage repayments.

Below: Compact Fluorescent Light Bulbs: The UK currently spends over £2 billion a year on electricity for lighting, a quarter of which is in the domestic sector. Less than 0.5 per cent of the lightbulbs bought in the UK are 'compact fluorescent bulbs' which can use 70 - 80 per cent less elctricity than standard filament based incandescent bulbs for the same light output.

61. See Friends of the Earth Evidence to House of Commons Energy Select Committee, November 1990.
62. see Further Reading

4.2 Cleaning Up Fossil Fuels

Coal provides almost a third of the UK's energy including three quarters of its electricity. It will undoubtedly play an important role in the transition to a renewable energy future. However, conventional coal burning techniques currently produce more acid emissions than the burning of other fuels using modern technology. In addition, burning coal releases more carbon dioxide than oil or gas per unit of energy produced. Particular measures are therefore needed to reduce the environmental impact of burning coal.

Cleaning Combustion

Acid emissions from existing coal plant can be greatly reduced through the fitting of regenerative flue gas desulphurisation (FGD) equipment and 'low NOx burners' to power stations. For any new power station, there are much cleaner and more efficient technologies, including specialised combustion techniques like 'fluidised beds' and gasification systems, and various advanced turbine systems like 'combined cycle' where exhaust gases are used to drive a second set of turbines. These technologies remove most of the sulphur during combustion and can have far higher efficiencies than conventional systems now in use. This reduces the amount of coal needed (and therefore carbon dioxide emitted) for each unit of electricity produced.

To reduce carbon dioxide emissions further, it makes sense to reduce the amount of energy wasted at the power station by converting to combined heat and power (CHP) or 'cogeneration'.

Combining Heat and Power

In most UK power stations, only about one third of the energy in the fuel ends up as useful energy in the form of electricity. Potentially useful heat energy can be retained by modifying the operation and this can be piped direct to local homes and factories. Using modern combustion techniques, efficiencies can be up to around 80 per cent, rather than the average but meagre 35 per cent typical of conventional generating plant. Combined heat and power stations can be fuelled by a wide variety of fuels - coal, oil, gas, methane from sewage farms, municipal waste, straw or agricultural wastes. The use of CHP avoids the unnecessary burning of fossil fuels in local

Above: Laying heat mains in Denmark.

premises and leads to reductions in carbon dioxide emissions.

CHP is well established in many countries and ranges in scale from small systems for single factories, hospitals and office blocks to large power stations heating extensive residential districts in cities such as Copenhagen, Stockholm, Berlin, Munich, Milan, Oslo and Paris (see photo right). The UK has dense urban populations and is therefore particularly suitable for estate-wide or city-wide schemes. The Department of Energy estimates that CHP could supply 30,000 MW of the UK's power needs by the year 2020, equivalent to between 25 per cent and 50 per cent of the capacity expected by then. However, the UK has so far shunned the advantages so readily taken up by large cities elsewhere in Europe.

The UK has also barely begun to realise the potential for small-scale CHP. In the last few years, however, interest has grown and the UK now produces about 2

4.3 System Integration Effects - Accomodating the Renewables

New generating plant can contribute to the electricity network in two ways: it can provide constant or 'firm' power (which saves expenditure on other plant), or alternatively, it can make savings in fossil fuel burnt. The most expensive capacity is that which is available at times of highest demand, or 'peak load'. No generating plant is 100 per cent reliable; there is always a possibility that it will not be available at times of peak demand when it is most needed. A number of renewable energy technologies can contribute relatively firm capacity; these include hydro-electricity, biomass incineration, and geothermal.

The contribution to firm power is very roughly equivalent to the average power; for wind energy, it is equivalent to about 40 per cent of the installed capacity, with a larger contribution possible during the winter months when the wind is more constant and average wind speeds are higher. (The wind may drop at one site, but flat calm across the whole country is rare.) The contribution from tidal power, though fluctuating, is entirely predictable. Further, the degree of firm power can be increased if several schemes are operating together, because high tide occurs at different times around the coast.

Questions have been raised about the extent to which intermittent sources like wind might be accommodated on the electricity grid. Studies in the early 1980s indicated that, once the contribution to electricity production increased above about 20 per cent, conventional plant might need to be kept in reserve or on standby to ensure the smooth operation of the system. Increasing local or national storage capacity would be another option (see below). The grid might also need to be reinforced in places to carry the additional power from remote wind farms or wave generators to the load centres. Though such modifications could be expensive, it will be many years before this situation arises, allowing sufficient time to plan ahead.

per cent of its electricity from some 500 CHP plants which also provide heating services to blocks of flats and old peoples' homes, hospitals, hotels, swimming pools and factories.

As with improvements in end-use efficiency, many unnecessary and irrational obstacles stand in the way of extensive development of CHP in the UK as a result of out-dated and inappropriate approaches to energy policy. In particular, the existence of two separate industries, one selling electricity (the electricity companies of the UK) and the other selling essentially heat (British Gas) has, until recently, left no clear space or regulatory framework for a company wishing to sell both. The privatisation of these two industries has gone some way to breaking down the barriers, but the results do not look promising for CHP: the major electricity companies still concentrate on constructing power stations without CHP facilities.

4.4 Energy Storage

The storage of heat and electricity is important for both renewable sources of energy and fuel-based systems. Storage converts intermittent and variable energy sources into firm sources of supply: when demand exceeds supply, energy can be drawn from the store to make up the difference. This reduces the overall need for electricity generating capacity since the need can be matched to average rather than peak demand. Energy storage is, however, expensive and invariably involves significant conversion and storage losses.

Low Temperature Heat

Water is the simplest and most commonly used storage medium for low temperature heat. A simple tank with an insulating jacket can store hot water for a matter of hours, or even days if well lagged. Storing summer heat for use in winter, however, requires more complex equipment, much larger systems and higher standards of thermal insulation. Most work on interseasonal heat storage has focused on the use of large subterranean caverns. An International Energy Agency report published in 1990 concluded that the technical feasibility of central solar heating plants with seasonal storage has been well established and that selective introduction may be economically feasible [63]. It noted that *"If the external costs of global pollution produced by burning fossil fuels were taken into account, central solar heating plants would already be cost effective for many applications"*. The UK's northern latitude need not be a bar to such schemes - one at Lyckebo in Sweden (see photograph), is on roughly the same latitude as Lerwick in the Shetland Isles.

Electricity

Rechargeable chemical batteries are today used to store relatively small quantities of electricity. However, they are expensive and provide rather modest performance. With large scale storage a number of options are possible, however, only one - pumped water storage - is currently used on any scale. This requires two reservoirs that are geographically close together but separated vertically by 100 metres or more. When supply exceeds demand surplus capacity can be used to pump water from the low reservoir to the higher one. Energy can

be recovered at a moment's notice by allowing water to cascade back down again via a water turbine. The potential for pumped storage in the UK is limited because of lack of suitable sites and high capital costs. The scheme at Dinorwig in mid Wales (which generates 1,700 MW) cost £450 million in 1984.

Hydrogen

Many people have speculated that hydrogen generated from water by electrolysis could eventually replace fossil fuels. In some ways hydrogen is a promising fuel: it burns with a 'clean' flame to produce harmless water vapour. It is easy to store and can be transmitted by pipe. However, hydrogen has a relatively low energy density, can explode with ease and the costs of production and storage are high. Nevertheless it could readily be produced using remotely sited photovoltaic arrays, wind turbines, or wave energy converters.

Interseasonal Heat Storage: The Swedes have a number of experimental solar district heating schemes with interseasonal heat storage. The largest at Lyckebo has a 100,000 cubic metre rock cavern heat store which is charged over the summer months from some 4,500 square metres of high temperature flat plate solar collectors located in a forest clearing (above). The scheme was designed to meet part of the space and water heating requirements of a community of 550 dwellings, a school and shops and has been operating since 1983. Recently a feasibility study for a much larger scheme has been carried out which would meet three quarters of the annual space and water demand of a small town. If it goes ahead, it will be at Kungalev in the west of Sweden and involve some 126,000 square metres of collectors and 400,000 cubic metre water filled rock caverns. 60 per cent of the heat would be used by the town's 6,000 inhabitants; the rest by industry and commerce.

63. IEA, 1990

5. Making Renewables Happen

"For 100 years it has been easy to burn and pollute. 100 years of tradition cannot be swept away without a struggle. The nearer renewable energy technology gets to success, the harder that struggle becomes."
Professor Stephen Salter, address to the Royal Society of Arts in 1981

Many non-technical obstacles are impeding the introduction of renewables: some are financial in nature, some are related to the market and the structure of the energy supply industries, some concern the impacts of technology on the environment and local communities, and some relate to the organisation and operation of the Department of Energy. This chapter analyses the nature of these problems and proposes mechanisms for tackling them.

Government involvement in renewable energy goes back to 1974. To date, the approach by successive Governments has been half-hearted and has lacked the commitment necessary for full development of the potential.

It is now time to move forward: for those technologies already proven, we need to establish an extensive deployment programme for the UK; for the other technologies, we must devote resources to a concerted programme of research, development and commercialisation.

5.1 Overcoming Financial and Economic Barriers

The high capital costs associated with small-scale production, and a variety of punitive taxes and other operating costs have been major impediments to the introduction of renewables in the UK. Moreover, the market is still seriously distorted by selective taxation and hidden subsidies. These favour investment in bulk supply over improved end-use efficiency, and in established energy supply industries over new ones. Some of these barriers have recently been removed; others remain.

One particularly biased handicap for renewable energy is the conventional method of economic assessment which does not include consideration of the environmental and other benefits derived from using renewable energy, resource conservation, reduced pollution, and increased energy security.

Box 5.1: Two examples of punitive taxes which have prevented early development of renewables exporting electricity to the grid:

■ Privately owned equipment has in the past attracted high local taxes (rates). Until recently, the local rating system for electricity-producing renewables was based on capital costs and not overall generation costs. This severely penalised private producers. The operators of a 200 kW wind turbine at Ilfacombe, north Devon, were forced to pay nearly £3,300 per year in rates, equivalent to an additional 1.6 pence on each unit of electricity generated. At the same time, power stations belonging to the CEGB - the nationalised electricity generating company - were 'formula rated', which meant that they were paying a rates bill corresponding to about 0.1 pence per kWh. Had the CEGB owned the Ilfracombe machine the rates bill would have been cut by more than 90 per cent. As from 1990, independent commercial generating companies are rated on the same 'formula' basis as the successors of the CEGB.

■ Exorbitant abstraction charges were imposed on small water power users by some Water Boards simply for the privilege of diverting water through their equipment. Some have been paying far more per volume than conventional power stations pay for cooling water. The Water Act 1989 abolishes water abstraction charges for small schemes under 5 MW.

The mining and processing of fossil and nuclear fuel, and the pollution from power stations affects peoples' health and their environment. Acid rain causes damage to buildings, bridges, trees and national monuments - a recent study of damage to UK buildings alone put the cost of repair at up to £17 billion [64]. Other costs are associated with reduced yields from agriculture, fisheries and forestry. The possible costs associated with climate change from global warming could be orders of magnitude higher. The costs of decontamination following a nuclear accident can be substantial; the estimated cost of cleaning up the damage caused by the disaster at Chernobyl in Russia is £200 billion over a ten year period. These and other costs which are borne by society as a whole but which are not incorporated

---

64. ECOTEC, (1990)

into the price of electricity, are called 'external costs'.

Though the UK Government has acknowledged that these external costs should be taken into account [65], it has produced no proposals for doing this. Failure to include external costs distorts the economics of the market and the choices that people make. It is better to include some estimate of external costs, however crude, than to ignore them altogether because they cannot be accurately determined. Ignoring these factors effectively constitutes a large scale subsidy to fossil fuel and nuclear power. While it is still uncertain by how much precisely the economic competitiveness of renewable energy will be improved, it is manifest that including external costs will significantly boost their prospects.

Ultimately, the level of any environmental premium will depend on the value which people put on the services they receive and the importance they place on having clean air and water and a biologically diverse and healthy environment for themselves and future generations.

Successful Support Schemes Abroad
Over the last decade several countries have successfully used legislation, tax credits and state aid to encourage the development of domestic renewable energy industries.

USA
In the United States, for example, enactment of the 1978 Public Utilities Regulation Policies Act (PURPA) exempted independent power producers from compliance with burdensome utility regulations, and forced utilities to pay the same price for the electricity that the utilities would have to pay were they to build new generating plant themselves. In some cases, buy-back tariffs were set for a full ten years. Tax incentives, offered at both the federal and state level, also encouraged investment in new technology. This combination of measures was particularly successful in California where it spawned whole new industries. The incentives were finally removed in 1985, and although some small companies subsequently went into liquidation, several new industries had by this time got over their teething problems and established a secure base. In less than a decade, renewable sources, including geothermal, wind, solar, biomass

and small hydro have grown to account for about 13 per cent of California's electricity.

More radical legislation has recently been enacted in various states in the US: New York, for example, is implementing competitive bidding systems that attempt to account for external environmental costs in the evaluation of alternative energy supply systems. The electricity utility regulators of Iowa now have the authority to consider environmental factors in the determination of buy-back rates along with economic and other factors [66]. Regulators in Nevada have assigned economic values to different types of pollution and can force the utilities to integrate these costs into their resource planning. It is expected that the new rules (adopted in 1991) will result in the expansion of indigenous geothermal electricity generation, the introduction of solar and wind generation in Nevada and a move away from reliance on fossil fuels [67].

Denmark
The Danish Government introduced support for renewable energy technology in 1979, covering 30 per cent of capital cost. State aid encouraged the development of a highly successful wind turbine industry; it has also been used to promote the use of straw as a fuel, and the development of biogas and certain solar projects. Danish wind turbine manufacturers were advised on ways of improving the performance and reducing costs of their machines by experts based at the National Wind Turbine Test Centre at Riso. The grants for wind turbines were reduced to 15 per cent in 1986, and finally phased out altogether in 1989 as the industry became established. They have since been replaced by tax credits: the owners of wind turbines obtain a proportion of the income from the sale of electricity tax-free - effectively doubling the yield on the investment. (It is estimated that about 6 per cent of the Danish population now own shares in wind turbines.)

65. Department of Environment, 1990
66. US Environmental Protection Agency, 1990
67. Wiel, 1990

In 1990, Danish companies installed over 350 machines in Denmark with a total installed capacity of 71 MW and worth around £30 million. The total cost of support measures and research and development costs between 1979 and 1990 was around £40 million, which is just under three times what the Department of Energy spent on building the 3 MW Orkney wind turbine, but in Denmark it was used to encourage a whole new industry which has erected over 3,000 wind turbines, and exported a further 7,000.

France
In France, the government has encouraged geothermal group heating schemes with special grants (Comité Geothermie) which cover the considerable financial risks associated with the exploratory drilling of the first well in a geothermal development. To date, over 60 schemes have been built in Paris and Bordeaux.

Successful Support Schemes for the UK?
Effective financial and fiscal (tax-related) support is required to ensure a rational allocation of national resources with environmental protection as the primary criterion. This is consistent with current Government thinking - the Government already intervenes in the energy market in many ways, for example, by funding nuclear research and development, subsidising deep-mined coal, imposing external financing limits (to limit borrowing), regulating oil extraction, taxing motor fuels (to raise revenue), and most significantly, by obliging the Regional Electricity Companies to contract for 'non-fossil fuelled electricity' (see below).

It is imperative, however, that support systems are not created which distort priorities (by encouraging investment in inappropriate technologies), produce grant-dependent industries that are unable to stand on their own feet, or attract unscrupulous operators who force up prices. These problems can be avoided by careful attention to the formulation and implementation of support systems. Proposals for refining the support systems arising from the privatisation of the electricity industry are set out in the next section.

Right: Vestas wind turbine factory, Lem, Denmark

5.2 The Implications of Electricity Privatisation

The fortunes of renewable energy in the UK have become intimately linked to the success or otherwise of electricity privatisation, and in particular, the introduction of a special purchasing obligation on the Regional Electricity Companies.

The Electricity Act 1989 enables the Secretary of State for Energy to require each of the 12 Regional Electricity Companies in England and Wales to secure the availability of a certain amount of electricity generated from non-fossil sources - principally nuclear - but including renewable sources of energy. The obligation arising from Orders laid before Parliament by the Secretary of State is called the Non-Fossil Fuel Obligation (NFFO). The obligation for nuclear power was set in March 1990, and the first obligation for renewable energy, in September 1990.

The original purpose of the Non Fossil Fuel Obligation was to secure a guaranteed market for nuclear generated electricity in England and Wales which would otherwise be too expensive to justify purchasing [68]. The arguments used in support of this mechanism were that it would promote *"diversity of supply"* which would provide security against fuel supply interruptions and fossil fuel price increases.

Since, at present, electricity from non-fossil sources is generally more expensive than fossil-fuel power stations, under the terms of the Non Fossil Fuel Obligation such non-fossil electricity will be purchased at a premium price, which is financed by a levy collected on sales of electricity. Only 2 per cent of the levy raised in 1990/91 was used to support renewable energy projects; the remaining 98 per cent (£1.25 billion) went to nuclear power.

In April 1989, the Government announced changes to the Non Fossil Fuel Obligation which provided for a series of additional 'tranches', reserved specifically for renewable energy, to be made through the 1990s. In the White Paper on the Environment, the Government stated that it intends to *"work towards a figure of 1,000 megawatts in 2000"* [69]. This amounts to a loose commitment that 2 per cent of electricity supply will be met by new renewable energy sources by the year 2000. The first renewables obligation was set in September 1990 at just 102.5 MW (DNC) [70].

Box 5.2: 1990 and 1991 (expected) 'Tranches' under the Non-Fossil Fuel Obligation

	1990 (MW)*	1991 (MW)*
Wind	28.7	60-120
Hydro	11.6	5-10
Landfill	35.5	30-60
Municipal Incineration	86	15-30
Biogas (and other projects)	6.5	15-30
Total	168.3	150-200

* measured in MW of *installed capacity*

68. Privatising Electricity, White Paper, Cmd 322, Section 46, February 1988
69. Department of Environment, 1990; [NB: The Government has not stated whether this 1000 MW is 'installed' or 'Declared Net Capacity' - see note 70 below].
70. DNC (Declared Net Capacity) is the term applied to the capacity of a plant which includes consideration of the intermittent nature of the particular resource. A conversion factor is applied to different technologies to reflect their intermittency under a formula defined in Statutory Instruments 1990 No.193. For wind energy, a factor of 0.43 is applied.

When the UK Government presented its proposals for the Non Fossil Fuel Obligation to the European Commission, there was strong opposition. The Commission considered that the Non Fossil Fuel Obligation, in effect, amounted to a nuclear subsidy and was a breach of its fair competition rules. Following negotiations, the Government agreed to limit the Non Fossil Fuel Obligation to an eight year period ending 31st December 1998 [71], though the EC has since indicated that it will treat an extension for renewables alone with a generally favourable view.

For renewables, this limit represents the most profound obstacle to their development: it creates major uncertainty within the renewable energy industries over long-term Government support; it severely reduces the ability of developers to secure capital loans; and for wind energy it forces developers to exploit sites with the highest wind speeds which are often of high landscape value.

In addition, the Non Fossil Fuel Obligation was not structured to apply to non-fossil electricity produced in Scotland and Northern Ireland. Scotland has massive renewable energy resources including 90 per cent of the UK's small hydroelectric potential, the best wave energy sites, some estuaries with a large tidal ranges, and the best wind reserves in Europe with 55 per cent of the UK wind potential [72]. Northern Ireland also has good wind resources. For Scotland, it was only in May 1991 that this anomaly was addressed, but the new position still fell short of ensuring a consistent nationwide policy on the Non Fossil Fuel Obligation.

Modifying the Non Fossil Fuel Obligation

By a combination of measures the Government can ensure that the industry is given a clear indication of political support and has the best foundation for future development needed to meet the environmental challenge:

■ The 1998 deadline for operation of the Non Fossil Fuel Obligation in respect of renewables should be replaced with a fixed period of support running for 12-15 years from the date the project is commissioned;

■ The Non Fossil Fuel Obligation should apply to the UK as a whole, integrating Scotland and Northern Ireland on an equal basis as England and Wales;

■ In the absence of mechanisms for ensuring that fossil fuels and nuclear power reflect their full environmental costs, the prices paid to renewable energy projects should include a premium in explicit recognition of their environmental benefits. This should be in addition to the current premium paid on the basis of their contribution to diversity of supply;

■ More challenging targets need to be set for individual technologies in line with UK potential.

71. Official report of EC Parliament, 16/5/1990, page 339.
72. Calculated by the Association for Independent Electricity Producers from figures in Department of Energy, 1988 and in ETSU/ITE, 1990.

5.3 Environmental Impact and the Public

All energy systems have an effect on the natural environment. It is inevitable, therefore, that conflicts of interest will arise between providing energy services and ensuring that people, wildlife and open spaces, are adequately protected. The environmental impact associated with most renewable energy technologies (noise, dust, construction traffic, visual intrusion and loss of amenity) is considerably less than with the current fuel-burning energy systems that they displace. Some technologies actually reduce other problems; for example, anaerobic digesters on intensive livestock farms reduce noxious effluents. Nevertheless, there is a range of environmental impacts associated with renewable energy which do have to be addressed and which mean, in some cases, that proposed projects may be inappropriate or unacceptable.

Obtaining planning permission will be a major factor in determining the rate at which renewable energy systems are introduced. Local people and a variety of countryside, amenity and wildlife groups, have raised objections to the siting of wind farms and refuse incinerators, and there has been fierce opposition to plans to construct tidal barrages or cultivate fast-growing trees on open moorland. Problems can be exacerbated where developers have failed to inform, let alone consult, the local community on their activities and intentions, behaviour guaranteed to lead to misunderstandings and hostility.

Whilst it is not possible to hide renewable energy systems completely, nor make them entirely innocuous, their impact can be considerably reduced by careful design and siting and by modifying their operating regime. Local concerns may be addressed by involving residents in the early stages of the planning process and by ensuring that genuine anxieties are properly considered and acted upon.

It is important when discussing environmental effects to keep the discussion in perspective and be aware of the costs and possible environmental consequences of not deploying renewables. Perpetuating current patterns of energy use will lead to greater environmental destruction through radioactive contamination, or the effects of acid rain and global warming. Opinion polls consistently show that renewable energy is a popular option for future energy supply [73].

Below are discussions of three environmental concerns; visual intrusion, noxious emissions and habitat damage. Three technologies are used: wind energy, waste incineration and tidal barrages. The discussion is intended to be illustrative of the environmental impacts of renewable energy.

Visual Intrusion and Wind Energy

Wind turbines can be visually intrusive. They can also look attractive and blend into the landscape. Much depends on the design, size and location of the machines and on the attitudes and preconceptions of the observer. The Danes have adopted three-bladed machines rather than two-bladed ones, in part because of their more pleasing visual appearance and the fact that they rotate more slowly (which means they also tend to be quieter). They also seem to prefer wind turbines mounted on tubular steel towers rather than on lattice towers or tripods, despite the additional expense.

Beauty, of course, is very much in the eye of the beholder and not everybody in the UK sees wind energy as benign and an important defence against acid rain and climate change. Though few organisations oppose renewable energy *per se*, faced with the prospect of a wind farm on their doorstep, some countryside and amenity groups feel that they have no choice but to object, even when the proposed windfarms are actually outside (but visible from) protected areas. Some have visions of forests of noisy unsightly machines - a mistaken image reinforced by seeing clips of early Californian wind farms, which are shown regularly on British television.

Trying to assess the precise impact of visual intrusion is difficult. Some factors such as numbers and scale effects are easily identifiable: small clusters of wind turbines are undoubtedly less visually intrusive than large wind farms with 30 turbines or more. Building wind turbines off-shore presents fewer environmental problems but increases technical problems.

Windfarm in Denmark.

Other factors are problematic: first, how do modern wind turbines compare with more familiar country objects such as farm buildings and silos, power station cooling towers, electricity pylons and cable runs? People have a natural tendency to reject the new and the unfamiliar, and yet to be apparently unconcerned by what might otherwise be seen as entirely unacceptable: the UK countryside is crisscrossed by 10,000 route miles of high voltage overhead cable supported on more than 50,000 large pylons and there are a quarter of a million route miles of overhead low voltage cables supported on millions of wooden poles.

A public attitude survey conducted on behalf of the Department of Energy showed that those who already have some experience of wind turbines in the locality are overwhelmingly convinced that the countryside is a suitable place for wind turbines and that *"they are an efficient use of rural land"* [74].

Second, how much weight should be given to visual intrusion as compared to say the acid rain and other chemical pollution avoided by not burning fossil fuels? Sweden, Germany, Poland and other East European countries have practical experience of the damage to forests and lakes caused by emissions from burning coal and oil. Each unit of electricity generated from wind turbines displaces 5-8 grams of sulphur dioxide, 3-6 grams of nitrogen oxides, 750-1,250 grams of carbon dioxide, and 40-70 grams of slag and ash. Some states in Germany actually pay a direct environmental credit of around 2.5 pence per unit in recognition of this benefit. States in Holland, recognising the advantages of wind energy, have identified particular areas where wind energy development is appropriate and have encouraged projects to site in such areas through financial incentives.

Noxious Emissions and Waste Incineration

Of the different components of a waste management system, incineration ranks low in popularity terms, and for understandable reasons. Most of the 30 or so municipal incinerators now left in operation in the UK have primitive gas cleaning equipment, capable of removing only the larger particles of fly ash and grit [75]. The majority are out of date and none will meet the EC Directives relating to emissions standards for existing municipal incinerators [76,77]. Particular anxiety concerns fall-out which may contain heavy metals (such as mercury and cadmium from batteries and lead from paint), asbestos, oxides of nitrogen, hydrochloric acid, and traces of dioxins and other highly poisonous organic compounds.

On potential health effects, current research indicates that properly run and maintained industrial or utility boilers, operated at high temperatures, with full screening to ensure material input control and modern gas-cleaning equipment, should in theory minimise emissions of toxic pollution. This begs the question as to whether such performance can be consistently achieved in practice. The legitimate concerns of the public will only be assuaged if very strict standards for emissions are imposed and adhered to, there is continuous monitoring of emissions and plant operators are made financially

73. For example, Department of Environment, 1991
74. Lee, Wren and Hickman, 1989
75. House of Lords Select Committee on European Communities, 1989
76. Lees, 1990
77. European Directives 89/369/EEC and 89/429/EEC came into force at the end of 1990 and define a set of standards for emission of the major airborne pollutants.

liable for any unforeseen impacts. Further, given the uncertainty over the link between incineration emissions and public health, extreme caution is warranted.

Disruption of Habitats and Tidal Power

There is strong opposition to the construction of tidal barrages in a number of UK's main estuaries, notably the Mersey and the Severn, but also in some smaller estuaries such as the Duddon. A barrage across the Severn, for example, would affect several million people living in Avon, Somerset, Gwent and South Glamorgan. It would cost over £9 billion, take about a decade to complete, and involve the movement of 32 million cubic metres of sand, gravel, rock, rubble and concrete, equivalent to about three times the volume of spoil moved in constructing the Channel Tunnel.

Estuaries are amongst the UK's most threatened wildlife habitats and are important spawning grounds for fish and other aquatic organisms (such as crustacia and shellfish). They also provide feeding grounds for resident and migrating wildfowl. Indeed, Bridgwater Bay in the Bristol Channel and the New Grounds at Slimbridge are already designated as Ramsar sites (a designation intended to provide protection against development); there are also 34 Sites of Special Scientific Interest in the area, some of which could be affected by a barrage.

By interrupting the flow of water, a barrage would change the tidal regime, level of salt, turbidity and sedimentation patterns. It would also affect fish migration. Additional problems could arise because of the influx of large numbers of tourists and the development of marinas and holiday accommodation. Modification of the tidal flow would affect the rates of erosion and sedimentation in the estuary. Higher water levels in the basin would affect groundwater and drainage.

Some of these effects are seen as positive: construction of a barrage would provide jobs and bring new prosperity to the region, especially from tourism and water sports. The barrage itself could be used to provide better control over flooding (especially during high Spring tides), and biological productivity in the estuary could actually increase as the water becomes clearer.

Redshank *tringa totanus*
60 per cent of the European population of Redshank winter in British estuaries.

Moreover, some of the problems could be mitigated by careful planning and by modifying the operating regime to ensure, for example, that mudflats and sandbanks are regularly exposed. Ship locks would provide access to ports, and fish ladders incorporated to enable salmon to reach their spawning grounds. However, such planning and flexibility in operation cannot remove the fact that a civil construction of such proportions would have a major impact on the natural habitat and the people living around it.

Ensuring Sensitive Development

Ensuring that specific renewable energy developments are in the public interest and for the national good is not always easy. But steps can be taken now by Government to reduce the risk of inappropriate and insensitive projects being developed, for example, by:

■ Establishing a coherent national energy plan which, amongst other things, sets clear targets for energy efficiency and renewable energy, and puts individual concerns in the broader context of environmental and strategic considerations;

■ Providing manufacturers of renewable energy technology with performance guide-lines of quality assurance - including, for example, in the case of wind turbines, guidelines on conversion efficiencies, reliability and noise levels that should be achieved;

■ Providing planners with clear guide-lines on siting, especially concerning environmentally sensitive areas and the proximity to dwelling places; and

■ Ensuring that there is strict control over construction and operation of plant (including emissions, noise and traffic), with financial liability falling on operators.

It is proposed below that some of these functions become the responsibility of a new Renewable Energy Agency.

5.4 The Need for New Institutions
Poor Financial Support
Early funding on renewable energy was adequate to cover fundamental work on resource size and the evaluation of device concepts and it produced some useful technical studies. But in 1983, just as many of the technologies were emerging from the laboratory, funding was cut. Several technologies, most notably active solar heating and wave energy, were abandoned before they had been given a fair chance to prove themselves. Even those that were officially recognised as 'economically attractive' or 'promising but uncertain' received relatively little financial assistance.

The total spent on renewable energy since the programme started in 1975 is just £180 million (£260 million in 1990 pounds) (see Figure 5.1). The Government believes that expenditure on research, development and demonstration could more than

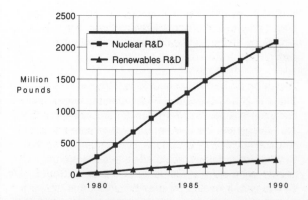

Figure 5.1: Cumulative Expenditure on Research and Development in the UK for Nuclear Power and Renewables (1979 - 1990) *

* Prior to 1979 gross cumulative expenditure on nuclear R&D amounted to approximately £16.3 billion (in 1987 pounds) compared to £16.2 million on renewables R&D

double by 1995 from current expenditure of £24 million to around £70 million per year - but the burden will fall largely on industry. In fact, after a slight increase in funding (to around £25 million per year in 1993), Government support will be cut back, and removed altogether by 2000 [78].

The Department of Energy's approach to research and development (R&D) funding has been glaringly inconsistent. The House of Commons Energy Committee wrote in 1990:
"We doubt that an R&D programme which involves spending three times as much on nuclear R&D as on all other energy R&D put together is a good reflection on the UK's future energy needs and opportunities" [79].

---

78. Department of Energy, 1988
79. House of Commons Energy Select Committee, 1990

Expenditure on renewable energy research has been dwarfed by the expenditure lavished on other areas. Since 1974, research into nuclear fusion alone has received nearly twice as much as all of the renewables put together and this is a technology that few think will ever be commercial [80]. Even now, almost 50 per cent of the Department of Energy's research budget for 1990-1991 is actually allocated to 'fast breeder' nuclear reactors (see Figure 5.2.), though this level of funding is expected to decrease over the next decade. The Department even funds a number of small programmes relating to nuclear power in less developed countries but, paradoxically, has thus far refused to fund work on photovoltaics because it does not consider that the technology has significant potential for the UK.

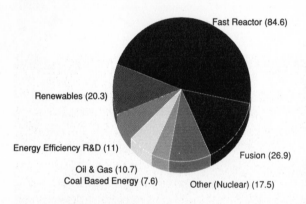

Figure 5.2:Research and Development Funding for 1990 - 1991 (in millions of pounds)

Misplaced Priorities

Most money spent on renewable research and development has so far gone into desk-top studies rather than getting machines out in the field or at sea.

For wind energy, much early investment went into the development of experimental large machines, culminating in the 3 MW wind turbine at Burgar Hill on Orkney commissioned in 1988. This involved a daring technological leap (the machine was ten times more powerful than anything any British company had ever built before). Moreover, it was a distraction from the more important task of commercialising small and medium sized turbines. Most of the money spent on wave power went into investigating the feasibility of constructing a massive 2,000 MW wave energy station off the west coast of Scotland, rather than first gaining practical experience with small stand-alone systems operating in comparative safety near the shoreline.

Weak Institutions

The whole renewable energy programme is run from a minor branch of a weak division in one of the smallest Departments of government. The Department of Energy is some 160 times smaller than the Ministry of Defence. Even the future of the entire Department of Energy is now under review, following de-nationalisation of the gas, oil and electricity industries. This has had the result of marginalising renewable energy and severely impeding its development, despite the commitment of individuals within the Department.

Virtually all of the research work in renewable energy is undertaken outside of the Department by consultants. It is coordinated by the Energy Technology Support Unit (ETSU), which carries out contract work in three main areas: the development of renewable energy sources; research, development and demonstration related to energy conservation; and developing a strategy for energy research and development in the UK. The fact that ETSU is based at Harwell where it is administered by the UK Atomic Energy Authority is a historical anomaly.

---

80. Flood, FoE, 1988

Renewable Energy Agency

An independent Renewable Energy Agency is needed to help overcome the many technical and non-technical barriers facing renewable energy in the UK. A Private Member's Bill which attempted to establish just such a body, was placed before the House of Commons in 1988 [81]. It was sponsored by Labour MP Frank Cook, and was supported by a number of Conservatives and Liberals, but was not accepted by the Government. The House of Commons Energy Select Committee had recommended establishing such a body in a report in 1984:

"serious consideration be given to the establishment of a new and strengthened energy technology management organisation...which would take over and significantly reinforce the present project management role of ETSU" [82].

The successful record of many other similar Agencies in the energy field (such as the Agence Française pour la Maitrise de L'Energie) and in other sectors (eg the Manpower Services Commission, Housing Corporation, Scottish Development Agency, Welsh Development Agency and National Parks, etc.) testifies that with adequate resources and proper accountability, such bodies can be very effective at policy and programme implementation [83].

The new body would be charged with responsibility for promoting renewable energy in the UK in conjunction with an expanded and enhanced renewables division within the Department of Energy.

The role of the Agency would be to:

■ Facilitate the government's programme of research and development, which would focus on commercialisation, deployment and long-term research;

■ Set special targets for the demonstration and deployment of renewable energy, with reports made to Parliament on progress;

■ Investigate policy options for achieving implementation targets for renewable energy as a whole and for individual technologies;

■ Provide advice and technical assistance to industry, including help with exports, and training technicians and support workers;

■ Develop a set of financial support measures designed to assist industry to develop a range of commercial technologies and prepare for mass production;

■ Administer grants and loans from a Government project fund, ensuring that they are appropriately used;

■ Advise on new legislation, regulations and statutes that could affect the prospects for renewable energy;

■ Help in the calculation of premiums to be paid for renewable energy in recognition of their environmental benefits;

■ Encourage Government departments and Ministries to purchase renewable energy for their own use where these can be shown to benefit the country as a whole (eg passive solar design for new buildings, wind turbines and photovoltaic arrays);

■ Liaise with entrepreneurs, academics and consultants, and bring them together through seminars and workshops with industry, banks and finance houses to facilitate greater penetration of renewable energy technologies; and

■ Produce publicity material (pamphlets, leaflets, films and videos) and set up a talks service for schools and public meetings.

81. Bill 174, 1988
82. House of Commons Energy Select Committee, 1984
83. Taken from Earth Research Resources, 1988

European Commission

The European Commission has run three major R&D programmes on renewable energy, and two Demonstration Programmes, since the mid 1970s. The programme has been funded through three Directorate Generals: DG XII (Science, Research and Development), which provides financial support for R&D; DG VIII (Development), which offers subsidies for wind farms in selected countries (under the Regional Development Fund's VALOREN Programme) and covers up to 50 per cent of costs; and DG XVII (Energy), which provides 40 per cent funding for selected demonstration projects.

The Demonstration Programme has undoubtedly helped foster collaboration between research teams in Member States, and facilitated the exchange of ideas. It has also acted as a useful focal point for the collection and dissemination of data, and provided valuable support to a number of projects that might otherwise have been abandoned - EC funding sustained the Cornish Hot Dry Rock Geothermal Programme over a difficult period when the UK Government withdrew support. However, the level of funding within the programmes is small, administrative and contractual arrangements are cumbersome and the selection of projects is strongly influenced by powerful lobbies. Total expenditure on renewables up to 1987 was only around 360 MECU (£250 million), which compares with an expenditure of around 1,570 MECU on nuclear fusion alone over the same period.

Furthermore, the Demonstration Programme has singularly failed to achieve its main objective, that of encouraging Europe-wide replication of successful technologies. An official review carried out in 1988 used more diplomatic language: it found that the programme had "not yet made a significant impact on European energy supply and demand".

More importantly, the EC has failed to set targets for renewables, noting simply that output from new and renewable energy sources should be "substantially increased". Targets are required to indicate a high level of political commitment.

An International Renewable Energy Agency

A new international agency should be established by the United Nations charged with responsibility for coordinating efforts on energy efficiency and renewable energy. It might be called the International Renewable Energy Agency (IREA). This body could be modelled on the International Atomic Energy Agency (IAEA). It would advise on new legislation, regulations and standards; advise on energy efficient and renewable technologies for achieving greenhouse gas reduction targets; assist with demonstration projects and with the commercialisation of technologies; develop and administer appropriate support measures; organise direct technical assistance for developing countries and technology transfer; and undertake a range of promotional activities. The Agency would also press international funding bodies to consider energy efficiency and renewable energy before agreeing loans for conventional energy projects. There would be one major difference between the IAEA and the proposed IREA: there would not be the need for safeguards against misuse of renewable energy technology.

6. A National Commitment to Renewables

"...the environment will only improve if we ourselves have the will to do what lies in our own hands...if we avoid these difficult decisions, we will be putting our short-term convenience ahead of the lasting needs of future generations."

The UK Government's White Paper on the Environment, September 1990

Up to now, the industrialised world has single-mindedly followed one energy path, one which has made us dependent on a few finite and polluting energy sources. The sheer scale of our energy use - even greater when the growing needs of the developing world are taken into account - now makes that path increasingly dangerous. Our ability to respond to the threat of global warming will depend on how quickly we are now prepared to move down a different energy route. As one of the world's major energy consumers, the UK will be influential in shaping the future, through the policies it pursues in the next decade.

The new approach that must guide these policies is simple: we need to get more from less, by conserving energy and by using it as efficiently as possible. And, we need to break our dependence on fossil fuel and nuclear power by supporting the development of sustainable and renewable sources of energy.

The resources are not lacking: the UK has the greatest diversity and abundance of renewable energy sources in Europe. As this book has shown, the technologies for harnessing these natural energy flows are available.

What is needed is genuine commitment from all sectors of the community and in particular from the Government. To date, governments have taken the route of *"short-term convenience"* and this must now change. A national commitment to developing renewable energy will ensure that *"the lasting needs of future generations"* are met with energy that is non-polluting and unlimited. Energy without end.

Bibliography for References

AEA Technology (1991) *The Chernobyl Accident: A review*

Binnie & Partners (1987) *Preliminary survey of Tidal Energy of UK Estuaries*, ETSU/STP-1539 1; *Preliminary Study of Small-scale Tidal Energy Phase I, II & III*, ETSU/STP-4035 A,B&C

British Petroleum (1990) *BP Statistical Review of World Energy*

Clark, William (Ed) (1990) *Usable Knowledge for Managing Global Climatic Change*, The Stockholm Environment Institute, London

Clarke, Alexi (1988) *Wind Farm Location and Environmental Impact*, Network for Alternative Technology and Technology Assessment (NATTA), Open University

Commission of European Communities (CEC) (1989) The European Wind Atlas, Directorate-General for Science, Research and Development (DG XII), Brussels

Danish Ministry of Energy (1990) *Energy 2000: A plan of action for sustainable development*

Department of Energy (1988a) *Renewable Energy in the UK: The Way Forward*, Energy Paper No.55, HMSO, London

Department of Energy, (1988b) *Privatising Electricity - White Paper*, Command 322, Section 46, HMSO

Department of Energy (1990) *Digest of UK Energy Statistics*, HMSO, London

Department of the Environment (1988) *Possible Impacts of Climate Change on the Natural Environment in the United Kindgom*, Department of the Environment, London

Department of the Environment (1990) *This Common Inheritance: Britain's environmental strategy*, UK Government White Paper on the Environment, HMSO

Department of Environment (1991) *Attitudes to Energy Conservation in the Home: Report on a Qualitative Survey*, HMSO

Doggart, J & Flood, M (1989) *Energy from Renewables: 1 The Solar Contribution*, Architects Journal, 13 September 1989, pp 73 - 81

Duckers, Les & Hotta, Hitoshi (1990) *A Review of Japanese Wave Energy*, Energy Systems Group, Coventry Polytechnic, Coventry

Duckers, Les (1990) Personal communication

Earth Resources Research (1988) *Setting up a National Energy Efficiency Agency: An Agenda for Action*, a report for the Charter for Energy Efficiency, London

ECOTEC Research and Consulting Ltd (1990) *An Economic Assesment of the Effects of Air Pollution on Modern and Historic Buildings*, Birmingham

Energy Efficiency Office (EEO) (1990) *Energy Efficiency in Domestic Electrical Appliances*, March Consulting Group, Energy Efficiency Series 13, HMSO

Energy Technology Support Unit (1985a) *Wave Energy: The Department of Energy's R&D Programme 1974-83*, ETSU-R-26, Department of Energy, HMSO

Energy Technology Support Unit (1985b) *Prospects for the Exploitation of Renewable Energy Technologies in the United Kingdom*, ETSU-R-30

Energy Technology Support Unit (ETSU) (1990a) *A Review of Mass Burn Incineration as an Energy Source*, ETSU-R-57, HMSO

Energy Technology Support Unit (ETSU) (1990b) *Renewable Energy Research & Development Programmes: Progress Report for the Department of Energy, 1989-1990*, ETSU-R-56, HMSO

Energy Technology Support Unit (ETSU) (1991) *Review of Photovoltaic Power Technology*, ETSU-R-50, HMSO

Energy Technology Support Unit (ETSU) / Institute of Terrestrial Ecology (ITE) (1990) *Land Constraints on Wind Energy Resource in the UK*, paper presented to British Wind Energy Association Conference

Evans, David (Ed) (1988) *Energy from Ocean Waves*, Euromechanics Colloquium 243, 26-28 September 1988, University of Bristol

Flood, Mike (1988) *The End of the Nuclear Dream*, Friends of the Earth, London

Flood, Mike (1989) *The Greenhouse Effect*, Warmer Bulletin No 20, pp 10-12

Friends of the Earth (1989) Evidence to House of Lords European Communities Committee, February, Friends of the Earth, London

Friends of the Earth (1990) Evidence to House of Commons Energy Select Committee, November, Friends of the Earth, London

Grubb, Michael (1988) *The Potential for Wind Energy in Britain*, Energy Policy, December, pp594-607

Henderson, G & Shorrock, L (1989) *Domestic Energy Fact File*, Building Research Establishment Report BRE/162/2/2

House of Commons Energy Select Committee (1984) *Energy Research Development and Demonstration in the UK*, Session 1983-84, HMSO

House of Commons, Energy Select Committee (1990) *The Department of Energy's Spending Plans, 1990 -91*, Seventh Report (462), HMSO

House of Lords, Select Committee on the European Communities (1989) *Air Pollution from Municipal Waste Incineration Plants*, HL Paper 17, HMSO

Intergovernmental Panel on Climate Change (IPCC) (1990) *Scientific Assessment of Climate Change*, Report prepared for IPCC by Working Group I, World Meteorological Organisation (WMO) and United Nations Environment Programme (UNEP)

International Energy Agency (IEA) (1990) Unpublished evidence to House of Commons Energy Select Committee; *Energy Efficiency*, Third Report.

International Energy Agency (IEA) (1990) *Central Solar Heating Plants with Seasonal Storage - Status Report*, Solar Heating and Cooling Programme, Task VII

Jackson, Tim (1988) *The Technical and Economic Comparison of Non-fossil Fuelled Electricity Supply Options*, Proof of Evidence, Hinkley C Inquiry, COLA 13

Jackson, Tim & Roberts, Simon (1989) *Getting out of the Greenhouse*, Friends of the Earth, London

Lashof, DA & Tirpak, DA (Eds) (1989) *Policy Options for Stabilizing Global Climate*, Environmental Protection Agency, Washington DC

Laughton, Michael (Ed) (1990) *Renewable Energy Sources*, published on behalf of the Watt Committee on Energy, Report No 22, Elsevier Applied Science

Leach, Gerald & Nowak, Zygfryd (1990) *Cutting Carbon Dioxide Emissions from Poland and the United Kingdom*, Stockholm Environment Institute, Stockholm, Sweden

Lee, T, Wren, B, & Hickman, M (1989) *Public Responses to the Siting and Operation of Wind Turbines*, Robens Institute and Department of Psychology, University of Surrey

Lees, Byrom (1990) *Can We Afford to Waste Municipal Waste? A discussion Paper*, National Society for Clean Air and Environmental Protection, Brighton

Lewis, Tony (1985) *Wave Energy: Evaluation of CEC*, Graham & Trotman, for the European Commission

Mitchell, CP & Mathews, J (1980) *Forest Biomass as a Source of Energy in the UK: the potential and the practice*, Department of Forestry, Aberdeen University, Mimeograph

Mortimer, Nigel (1989) *Aspects of the Greenhouse Effect*, Proof FoE 9, Hinkley 'C' Public Inquiry

Norgard, Jorgen (1990) *Low Electricity Appliances - Options for the Future, in Electricity. Efficient End-Use and New Generation Technologies, and their Planning Applications*, Johansson (Ed). Lund University Press, Sweden

NORWEB / Energy Technology Support Unit (ETSU) (1989) *Prospects for Renewable Energy in the NORWEB Area*

Olivier, David *et al* (1983) *Energy-Efficient Futures: Opening up the solar option*, Earth Resources Research, London

Organisation for Economic Cooperation and Development (1988) *Environmental Impacts of Renewable Energy*, OECD, Paris

Rand, Marcus (1990) *Developing Wind Energy for the UK*, Friends of the Earth, London

Richards, Keith (1989) *Landfill Gas - A Global Review*, paper to Seventh International Biodeterioration Symposium, Emmanuel College Cambridge

Richards, Keith (1989) *All Gas and Garbage*, New Scientist 3rd June 1989

RTZ Consultants Ltd (1991) *Conceptual Design for a Hot Dry Rock Geothermal Energy Project*, Summary, ETSU-G-153S, HMSO

Salter, Stephen (1988) *Proof of Evidence (DR4)*, Hinkley Point Public Inquiry

Salter, Stephen (1990) Personal Communication

Scurlock, Jonathon & Hall, David (1990) *The Contribution of Biomass to Global Energy Use*, Biomass 21, pp 75-81

Selzer, H (1989) *Potential for Wind Energy in the European Community: An assessment study*, Solar Energy R&D in the EC, Series G, Vol 2, D Reidel, Dordrecht/CEC

Steen, Jan-Erik (1985) *Norwegian Project: Energy from the waves in the South Pacific*, Scandinavian Energy, No 1

Sunderland Polytechnic / Sheffield City Polytechnic (1990) *Cost Modelling of HDR Systems: A preliminary examination of rig rates and HDR drilling costs*, ETSU-G-138, Part 1

Taylor, Derek and Rand, Marcus (1990) *Planning for Wind Energy in Dyfed*, Altecnica, Milton Keynes

Walker, John (1988) *A CEGB Perspective on Offshore Wind Power*, meeting of the Royal Aeronautical Society, *An Offshore Wind Megaproject*, London 29 March 1988

Wiel, Stephen (1990) *Nevada Adopts Clean Power Rule*, Nevada Public Services Commission

Windirection (1988) Vol VII (4), p6

WindStats Newsletter (1990) Vol 3, No 2

World Resources Institute / International Institute for Environment and Development (1989) *World Resources 1988-89: An assessment of the resource base that supports the Global Economy.*

United Nations (1965) *World Energy Supplies 1960-63*, New York

United Nations (1981) *1979 Yearbook of World Energy Statistics*, New York

United Nations (1986) *1986 Energy Statistics Yearbook*, New York

US Environmental Protection Agency (EPA) (1990) *Selected Summary of Current State Responses to Climate Change*, Climate Change Division, Office of Policy Planning and Evaluation, Washington

Suggested Further Reading

Brower, Michael (1990)
Cool Energy: The renewable solution to global warming, Union of Concerned Scientists, Cambridge, Massachusetts, USA

Compass Project (1988)
Environmental Impacts of Renewable Energy, OECD, Paris

Cross, Bruce (Ed) (1991)
European Directory of Renewable Energy Suppliers and Services 1991, James and James Science Publishers Ltd

Department of Energy (1989)
Renewable Energy in Britain

Energy Technology Support Unit (1985)
Prospects for the exploitation of Renewable Energy Technologies, R-30 Report, HMSO

Energy Technology Support Unit (1985)
Prospects for Renewable Energy in NORWEB Area, HMSO

Flavin, Christopher & Lenssen, Nicholas (1990)
Beyond the Petroleum Age: Designing a solar economy, Worldwatch Institute, Report No 100, December 1990

Flood, Michael (1983)
Solar Prospects: the potential for renewable energy, Wildwood House, London

Goldemberg, Jose, Williams, Robert & Reddy, Amulya (1988)
Energy for a Sustainable World, World Resources Institute, Washington

Grubb, Michael (1990)
The Cinderella Options, Energy Policy, Part One, July/August 1990, pp 525-542; Part Two October 1990, pp 711 - 726

Hall, David & Overend, R (1987)
Biomass: Regenerable Energy, John Wiley and Sons, Chichester/New York

International Energy Agency (1987)
Renewable Sources of Energy, OECD, Paris

Johansson, Thomas, Bodlund, Birgit & Williams, Robert (Eds) (1989)
Electricity: Efficient End-use and New Generation Technologies, and their planning implications, Lund University Press, Sweden

Laughton, Michael (Ed) (1990)
Renewable Energy Sources, Watt Committee Report No 22, London

Leggett, Jeremy (Ed) (1990)
Global Warming: The Greenpeace report, Oxford University Press, Oxford

Ottinger, Richard et al (1990)
Environmental Costs of Electricity, Pace University Centre for Environmental Legal Studies, Oceana Publications, New York

Palz, Woolfgang (1990)
Renewable Energy in Europe, International Journal of Solar Energy, Volume 19, pp 109 - 125

Patterson, Walt (1990)
The Energy Alternative, Channel 4/Boxtree Press

Patterson, Walt (1987)
Advanced Coal-Use Technology, Financial Times Business Information

Index

Index continued

Friends of the Earth Publications

To order any of the publications listed below (including additional copies of *Energy Without End*), please send your completed order to: Publications Despatch, Friends of the Earth, 26-28 Underwood Street, London N1 7JQ.

If you would like a full Friends of the Earth Publications List, please send an A5 SAE to the above address.

Cutting Your Electricity Use
A simple step-by-step guide to easy actions which you can take to reduce your electricity use, save money and cut polluting emissions.
October 1990
L £0.30

Developing Wind Energy for the UK
Development problems such as lack of attention to site impact and assessment risk are affecting the introduction of wind energy in the UK. This report examines overseas experiences and proposes how, through community involvement, these problems can be overcome.
January 1990
L £3.50

Getting Out of the Greenhouse
Establishing an effective energy policy to tackle the Greenhouse Effect is paramount. This report provides the first coherent economic analysis of the policy options available in the UK. Widely acclaimed since its publication, this report provides a useful agenda for action for policy makers.
December 1989
L £3.00

Efficiency of Electricity Use The UK could enjoy the same standards of living using 70 per cent less electricity, concludes this report to the House of Lords. In a detailed examination of the technical potential for improving the efficiency of UK electricity use, action for the UK and Europe is recommended.
February 1989
L £2.50

Energy Efficiency
Barriers to improving energy efficiency are political rather than technical and can be overcome if they are understood. This memorandum to the House of Commons Energy Select Committee details the obstacles to a more energy efficient UK and provides 30 policy recommendations to remove these barriers.
January 1991
L £4.00

Setting Standards for Energy Efficiency
The generation of electricity in the UK leads to extensive national and international pollution. Yet much of that electricity is 'wasted' in inefficient appliances. This policy briefing outlines how, through the setting of efficiency standards for household electrical goods and their labelling, the first steps can be taken towards reducing pollution and raising public awareness.
October 1989
L £1.50

Order Form

Title	Price	Quantity	Total
Energy Without End	£6.95		
Cutting Your Electricity Use	£0.30		
Developing Wind Energy for the UK	£3.50		
Getting Out of the Greenhouse	£3.00		
Efficiency of Electricity Use	£2.50		
Energy Efficiency	£4.00		
Setting Standards for Energy Efficiency	£1.50		
		Total cost	
		Donation	
		P&P	Free
		Total Sent	

Name _____
Address _____
_____
_____ Postcode _____
Telephone _____
Date _____ / _____ / _____

Friends of the Earth

The Earth needs all the friends it can get.
And it needs them now.

For thousands upon thousands of years our planet has sustained a rich diversity of life. Now, one single species – humankind – is putting the Earth at risk.

People the world over are suffering the effects of pollution, deforestation and radiation. Species are disappearing at a terrifying rate. The warming of the atmosphere threatens us all with devastating changes in climate and food production.

But it needn't be like this – we know enough to reverse the damage, and to manage the Earth's wealth more fairly and sustainably. But the political will to bring about such a transformation is still lacking.

And that's exactly where Friends of the Earth comes in.

IT'S TIME YOU JOINED US

I'd like to join Friends of the Earth. Please send me your quarterly magazine. I enclose:

£12 ☐ individual   £250 ☐ life

I'd like to donate £50 ☐   £35 ☐   £15 ☐   Other £ ☐

I enclose a cheque/PO for total of £ _____

payable to **Friends of the Earth** or debit my Access/Visa No:

Card Expiry date: ☐☐

Signature _____   Date _____

Send to: Friends of the Earth Membership Department, FREEPOST, 56-58 Alma Street, Luton, Beds LU1 2YZ.

081 200 0200 to join/donate anytime

FULL NAME _____

ADDRESS _____

POSTCODE _____

Friends of the Earth **F81 LAFE**

P2, 7. 8,9.

P12, 21, 23